Dora Albert

Stop Feeling Tired and Start Living

Englewood Cliffs, N. J. • **PRENTICE-HALL, INC.**

PRINTED IN THE UNITED STATES OF AMERICA
84678

Dedication

This book is dedicated to everyone who has ever said, "I feel so tired." This feeling seems to be an inevitable part of our lives in this so-called "age of anxiety." But anxiety can be dealt with, and so can that tired feeling. When those who have suffered from it rise above it, they can be magnificent.

This book is written in the hope that it can help everyone who is ever troubled by such feelings to learn how magnificent his energy can be when he conquers them.

The author hopes that this book will point the road to this conquest.

My husband and I have both known these problems, have faced them, and to a large extent have conquered them.

This book is dedicated to everyone who wants to improve himself in this respect. That desire can easily be the beginning of a new life.

Preface

Whenever, in the past year or so, any of my friends have asked me what I was working on and I have told them that I was doing a book on how to whip that tired feeling, they have said, "That's for me."

The problem is almost universal. Scientists tell us that it is impossible for anyone *never* to be tired.

But there is a difference between normal tiredness and that tired feeling. With normal tiredness, sleep is a blessed relief, and one springs out of bed in the morning, refreshed. Also, before one becomes normally tired, one has the feeling of having accomplished a great deal.

With that tired feeling, there is often inertia, lassitude, boredom. One is tired without any great sense of achievement.

In whipping that tired feeling, I have been my own best guinea pig. Just as I think it is presumptuous for any one who has never raised children to tell how to raise them, I am inclined to believe that someone who has never had that tired feeling just doesn't know what he is talking about when he tells how to beat it. On whom better can one test one's prescriptions than on oneself?

About ten years ago, I said to my doctor: "I feel tired most of the time. Must I continue to live like a semi-invalid?"

"You have been living on nervous energy for years," he said. "You didn't rest when you should have. Now nature is demanding the payment for a debt you contracted years ago."

And he advised me to relax at frequent intervals.

Still, his answer was not completely right for me.

v

Another doctor said to me, "You are a thoroughbred, not a plowhorse. You must not expect the energy of a plowhorse from yourself."

To myself I thought: "That's a great line for society women and movie stars. But some of my ancestors were sturdy peasants."

Physically, there was very little that was wrong with me. I was suffering from indigestion, due to the habit of worrying. I had to cure myself of that habit. In doing so, I helped whip that tired feeling to a certain extent. In addition, I wasn't completely happy in my work. I was writing exclusively about movie and TV stars, and I needed a change of pace. I began to write about other subjects, too, and as my horizons broadened, my energy increased.

As the years have gone by, I have learned other secrets of how to whip that tired feeling. This book is based not only on what famous authorities have said. It is also a record of discoveries that I have used personally, and that have helped me.

Today, far from being a semi-invalid, I have a normal and at times a super-normal quota of energy.

Recently a friend said to me, " I hate people who say 'I am tired' or 'I am dead.' I say to them, 'You might as well be dead as to *feel* that way.' "

I can understand how wearying it is to someone with abundant energy to listen to the half-Zombies who are always complaining. But I can also understand the victims of that tired feeling, and their unhappiness. Inevitably, they suffer from it and for it.

All this need not be. The remedies are so simple.

You will find them in this book, which is a synthesis of the experiences of hundreds of people I have known, and which at the same time tells of some of my own.

Almost every week science casts new light on the sources of that tired feeling. More and more, as time goes on, we find that the most fundamental sources are emotional. Basically, then, this is a book on how to control your emotions, so that you are their master instead of the other way round.

Contents

||||||||||||||||||||||||||||||||||||||||||||||||||||||||||||||||||||||||||||||||||||||||||||||||||||||||||||||||||||||||||||||||||||||||||||||||||

Part 1

HOW TO BUILD UP YOUR STOREHOUSE OF ENERGY

Part 2

HOW TO STOP SQUANDERING ENERGY

6. How to Control Energy-Squandering Anger . . 81

Your amazing capital of energy • We'd be labeled insane if we threw money away so recklessly • Anger can waste our energy in two ways • Anger is paradoxical in its effects on our energy • The immediate effect of anger • Fury gave this man abnormal physical strength • The secret of super-strength in emergencies • Anger is a preparation for action • Anger sometimes prepares us for the wrong action • Anger prepares the body for violent action • Chronic anger can make us ill • Hate and rage are intimately tied up with each other • Anger is apt to make us temporarily stupid • Anger can destroy a previously pleasant relationship • Anger first builds up, then wastes energy •

7. Seven Ways to Reduce Energy-Destroying Tension 97

Part 1

HOW TO BUILD UP YOUR STOREHOUSE OF ENERGY

1

Why Get Tired?

THE ADVERTISEMENT IN THE WINDOW OF A TRAVEL OFFICE IN Los Angeles caught my eye.

"Memo to a tired business man," it read. "Trip on a Union Pacific Domeliner is a great nerve tonic. Try it on your next trip East. Do your nerves jangle as much as your phone? Is your desk stacked with Miltown or the like? Then take a break. Make that next business trip on a Union Pacific Domeliner! You will find it a fine tranquilizer."

Swinging in the window to attract attention to the ad was a photograph of a business man in a state of complete relaxation.

APPEALS TO THE TIRED HORDE

Wherever you turn, you find ads designed to appeal to the tired business man, or the equally tired housewife.

Over your TV set, you hear the appeal: "What is sapping your energy? Why do you feel devitalized, weary? Perhaps you have tired blood!"

During the past few years, the appeals to those with "tired blood" have become so pronounced that the *New Yorker* recently ran a cartoon about these individuals. It pictured a beggar sitting on a street corner, with a tin can in his hands, and a sign across his chest. The sign read: "Tired Blood."

All over this country and perhaps throughout the world,

3

hundreds of thousands of individuals believe they haven't enough energy to meet the daily demands of life. Some of them wake up feeling tired; go wearily through their daily chores; can barely get up enough strength to drag themselves to their sofas to watch TV at night, and finally go to bed, settling for a restless sleep that leaves them more tired than when they lay down. Others go listlessly to parties that drain off more of their already drained energy.

So many tired people. Chronic tiredness is the great medical problem of the 20th century. You are going to discover that this need not be. You can have energy to spare.

Dr. Dwight L. Wilbur of Stanford University reported in the *Journal of American Medical Association* that more than half of all patients seen by doctors suffer from a "tired feeling."

From women doctors in 17 countries the American Medical Women's Association accumulated facts indicating the four leading complaints among women. They were foot trouble, anxiety, depression, and fatigue. Just examine those complaints. Every one of the other three can cause fatigue.

One company ordered its executives to take frequent vacations. Fatigue is considered such a drain on vital energy that one large company recently ordered its top executives to take a one-week vacation every seven weeks.

Alarmed by the toll that heart disease, strokes, and ulcers were taking among top executives, Bart Schwartz of International Textiles, Ltd., told his top men that they would have to take frequent vacations, whether they wanted to or not. The system has been a good one. Executives have accomplished more during their working weeks than previously. They work at a higher pitch of enthusiasm. With so many vacations to anticipate, they don't exhaust themselves.

You, too, may be wearing yourself out too fast, too soon. A recent medical report proved that non-executives are even more susceptible to hypertension, heart attacks, and other illnesses arising from stress reactions than the executives themselves. There's an excellent chance that you—whether or not you have executive responsibilities—have that tired feeling only too often.

Perhaps you smilingly deny it as you play nine more holes of golf, or try to stave off that tired feeling with another scotch and soda, or endless cups of coffee.

But you can't help wondering about the seemingly tireless men and women you sometimes meet. How do they retain their vitality while every step you take seems to wear you down?

There are no tireless individuals. In spite of their apparent tirelessness, these paragons of energy are sometimes bone-weary, too. If they postpone rest for too long, they may eventually collapse, requiring longer than you do to recuperate.

A seemingly tireless woman who exhausted herself. In Hollywood, Alyce Canfield, the successful magazine, screenplay writer, and collaborator with Mervyn LeRoy on the book, *It Takes More Than Talent,* was long regarded as a tireless person. She wrote about 20 articles a month, plus doing the leg-work for them, plus writing screenplays, plus doing gossip columns, plus writing books.

It was nothing for her to spend 16 hours a day at a typewriter, so that her back ached when she rose from her desk chair. She took no days of rest. Sometimes she attended parties, but never to have fun, just to gather material for her columns and articles. She was literally driven by a compulsion to work.

Now psychiatrists tell us that no one ever breaks down simply because of an overload of work. But the same compulsion that causes us to overwork can also cause nervous complications. Today Alyce confesses frankly that the cause of her compulsion to work ceaselessly was an insatiable desire for perfection. No matter how hard she worked, she never felt she was doing enough. When someone is that much of an eager beaver, the roots usually lie in a basic feeling of insecurity, which often has its start in childhood.

Busy in those days analyzing the inner secrets of others,

Alyce Canfield never asked herself what was driving her to work as though demons possessed her.

Her slumber at nights was fitful.   She was so busy planning the next day's work she didn't know what the word "relaxation" meant.

As a result of all this effort, she had a wonderful bank account and a lovely home in Sherman Oaks, complete with the finest swimming pool, which she never used.

Her husband, Jerry Jerome, an account executive with Daniel Reeves, loved her deeply enough to accept his wife's dedication to her work, though he often tried to prevail upon her to take things more easily.   But no one could influence her until the day she discovered she needed surgery, due to two growths that had affected her thyroid.

She was ordered to take a year's rest.   The doctors told her, however, that it would be impossible for them to operate because she was so run down.   They said she would need a year's rest, including six months in bed.

Six months passed before she was strong enough to undergo surgery.

If Alyce had not overworked for years, she might have recuperated in a month.   Because she had driven herself to the point of exhaustion, she had to spend six more months away from the typewriter after surgery.

"I'll never drive myself that hard again," she told me.   "I used to think that I was tireless, and would never collapse. I found, during the year when I wasn't able to work at all, that no one is really tireless.   If you prevent fatigue by leading a normal life, with adequate rest and vacations, you don't break down physically, as I did."

How to recognize abnormal tiredness.   If you work about eight hours and play about eight hours, you'll get normally tired.   A night's rest will restore your energy.

If it doesn't, then something is wrong.   Physically, emotionally, or spiritually, you've built up a resistance to using your energy properly.

Negative emotions may be your enemy.   You've heard a lot about positive and negative thinking. But the real danger caused by negative thinking is in the arousal of negative *feeling*.

Take Philip, for instance. As a young married man, he started off in the advertising business with great fire and ambition, full of youthful ideas and enthusiasm.

As time went by, most of the individuals who had started with him left the company. There was a whole new contingent of young, aggressive men who never hesitated to express their ideas at conferences.

At these conferences Philip was silent. With the years he had become frightened. He no longer believed in his own ideas, and was afraid to expose them to possible criticism.

Because he was the last of the old guard, he felt like the last leaf on a tree—afraid that he, too, would fall. Because he was afraid, he tried to stay as much in the background as possible, never venturing an opinion, carrying out orders like a mere clerk.

Since his days and nights were filled with fear—and fear is exhausting—he became easily fatigued. The demands on him at his firm were not great. But his anxiety about his ability to fulfill them was so great that it wore him out.

Finally, the thing he feared happened. Very often, our expectations help to bring about the things we fear.

In accordance with his fears, Philip was fired. He became more frightened than ever.

With his regular source of income gone, and only unemployment insurance to depend upon, he became almost paralyzed with fear.

Fear has definite chemical effects upon our bodies. It can mobilize us for action; or we can become frozen with fear. Philip allowed himself to freeze with fear. Each morning he would awaken tired and apathetic, feeling as though there were nothing left to live for.

What should Philip have done? He should have realized that the real source of his income lay in his God-given abilities. He should have tried to figure out some way to use those

abilities to help some other firm.   Possibly he might have built
up a successful career as a free-lance copywriter, or as a con-
sultant to another advertising firm.   But what he needed to do
first was to overcome the habit of negative feeling that had destroyed his energy.

One good way to do this was suggested by William James,
the great psychologist.   He advised those filled with doubts
and fears to fill out two sheets of paper, heading one negative,
the other positive.

On the negative sheet, Philip could have described his negative way of behaving at conferences, and the fears that kept
him from expressing his own creative ideas.

On the sheet labelled "Positive" he could have described the
way he felt a man in a creative field *should* behave, when
forced into competition with younger men in the same business.

With a feeling of intense loathing, he could have read his
own description of the negative way of acting; then torn the
sheet of paper or burned it in the fireplace.   This would have
been a symbol of his intention to discard this method of behaving.   Afterwards he could have reread his description of
the way he *should* react.   He could have said to himself,
"From now on, I shall conduct myself in this positive manner."
Every night before going to bed, he could have reread the sheet
marked "Positive" and have told himself, "Every day, I am
going to find it easier and easier to follow this positive method
of action."

Maybe your case is very different from Philip's.   You're not
consciously afraid of anything.   But each of us who ever becomes abnormally tired is carrying a load greater than Atlas'
of unconscious or conscious fear, hatred, worry, or other negative emotions.

You need all the energy you can build up.   You also need
to learn how to conserve this energy.   This is a demanding
world.   You can meet its demands and defeat the enemies
within you that threaten your energy, if you know how.   It's
not difficult, nor does it require a lot of your time.

Whether we cast an eye on the career of an Edison or an

Einstein, the advocate of the "strenuous life," Teddy Roosevelt, or some current brilliant business success, we find successful human beings filled to overflowing with energy.

What secrets did they learn that you and I should also learn?

We have to learn them not only to achieve success, but also to save our health, to protect ourselves from the inroads of illness, and to save ourselves from the kind of nervous exhaustion that exacts months of bed rest as its toll.

Fatigue, a menace to your health. So threatening to health is chronic fatigue that according to Sir James Paget: "Fatigue has a larger share in the promotion or transmission of disease than any other single causal condition you can name."

Energy pills are not a cure-all. In recent years some of the popular magazines have carried articles about exciting drugs that would supposedly turn men from semi-Zombies into supermen.

Actually, reports from Rockland State Hospital, Orangeburg, New York, indicated that the drug most highly praised by the magazines, iproniazid (the trade name Marsilid) had been very successful in stirring out of their lethargy a high percentage of extremely depressed patients.

But at the same time reports from various parts of the United States and Mexico indicated that in some patients Marsilid had had some dangerous side effects. Some patients had become ill with jaundice after using it.

A drug company's candid statement about Marsilid. L. D. Barney, President of Hoffman-La Roche, Inc., the manufacturers of Marsilid, issued a candid statement to physicians. "Marsilid, as most physicians know, is a highly potent compound of an entirely new type . . . unlike anything else known to clinical medicine. . . . It has been described as a psychic energizer (the opposite of a tranquilizer) . . . Marsilid frequently has a profound effect in severely depressed and regressed patients, but it is definitely not a 'pep' pill.

"Inasmuch as Marsilid affects several enzyme systems, it is capable of producing undesirable side effects such as hypotension, jaundice, and hepatitis. All patients should therefore be kept under the closest possible observation and the use of the drug should be discontinued at the first indication of jaundice, impaired liver function, or other serious side reactions."

Psychiatrists tell us that psychic energizers like Marsilid are potentially dangerous drugs, intended primarily for individuals suffering from serious depressions. The promised Utopia— when just taking a pill will solve all your energy problems—is not yet at hand.

The danger of using energy pills.   There is another group of drugs, such as Benzedrine and Dexedrine, that may be recommended occasionally by doctors or psychiatrists to give a person a feeling of well-being when he is particularly tired.   But psychiatrists warn us that anyone who uses them continuously for the treatment of chronic feelings of fatigue is making a serious mistake, because he is not dealing with the real sources of his trouble and may be "beating a tired dog" to the breaking point.

Don't beat that tired dog!   To stop that chronic tired feeling, you have to get at its real causes.

You have all the energy you need to get anything you seriously want out of life.   But if you have been directing your energy destructively, you'll have to change.

This book will give you a philosophy of life and a way of attacking your work and your recreation that will enable you to accomplish the most important things in your life, and to feel full of abounding energy most of the time, the way people were *meant* to feel.

Since your purpose is to be a normal human being and not a paragon of tirelessness, you will sometimes feel pleasantly fatigued.   Otherwise why would Nature impose sleep as part of her rhythmic pattern for us?

THE PATTERN OF LIFE THAT MAKES SENSE

There is a pattern of life that makes sense.   It is a pattern of ebb and flow, as rhythmic as the beat of music.   It is based on Nature's and God's own rhythms and melodies.

Explaining this pattern, Raymond C. Baird, consulting engineer from Santa Monica, California, told me: "For years I have specialized in the study of vibrations. I know of nothing that does not depend on them. You can hear me because of certain vibrations, see me because of others. Every sense requires an element of vibration to function.

"Time is supposed to be one of the biggest enigmas, but to tell the time we have to refer to something that is vibrating. Even your watch contains an escapement, a wheel that vibrates back and forth.

"Every human being is made up of a tremendous number of vibrations."

Music gives the clue. "Music, too, is based on vibrations. In a great composition the composer has skillfully woven together the music so that somewhere comes the climax—a tremendous, thrilling jolt. After the climax comes a release of tension. Then comes the melody rest."

The four steps that give a rhythmic melody its charm. "What gives rhythm its subconscious charm is that within the measure of melody that is repeated, you go through a cycle. You have the drive, the climax, the release, and then rest."

How planning helps build up energy for the drive. We build up a certain amount of energy by planning our work. This is like taking a spring and stretching it. When Mr. Average Man gets out of a chair and starts to repair a piece of furniture, he has already stretched the spring in his head by doping out his plan for repairing. That plan helped build up his energy.

As he continues with the chore, he gets more and more of it done. His mind may start working on what he is going to do next. He's stretching the spring again. When he finishes repairing the chair, he assumes a position of rest. But not for long! The spring starts to stretch in his head.

The idea he has worked out in his mind urges him on so strongly that he gets his pruning shears, goes into the yard, and starts clipping the hedges.

The melodic line of life. In all curves of activity, we rise from a beginning to a climax. After the climax, comes a release of tension, the sense of a job done. We taper off to a quiet stage. Then as time goes on, we marshal our energies and our attitudes so that we can go uphill to another climax.

A beginning, a middle, a climax, release, and rest—that is the melodic line of life. It governs all our activities. Suppose, for instance, you're planning an advertising campaign. First comes the warm-up or beginning, during which you determine the purpose of the campaign. You plant this idea in your unconscious mind. The next day you start the actual work on the campaign with a fine beginning spurt. You go ahead with your plans until you reach a climax for your work with the completion of a layout and specific plans in writing. You feel a temporary release from tension, and take a short rest—perhaps a pleasant week-end.

Then, when you try to sell the idea behind the campaign to a client, you again go through the stages of warm-up, beginning, climax, release, and rest.

Every salesman, in making or attempting a sale, goes through these stages. The rest between sales may last only five minutes, but it is usually long enough for him to take a "breather."

Aside from your work, you will find the melodic line of life governing your sex activities, and it is symbolic of life and death.

You must never skip the final stage—rest—in anything you do.

You can stave off senseless exhaustion by arranging your life so that Nature's rhythm dominates your activities. You take brief rests *before* you become exhausted. You must have release of tension and rest after every big period of activity.

To build up energy, you also have to plan your work. "The greater the plan, the greater the potential," says Mr. Baird.

But let's consider: Why are you often tired, sometimes far too tired to realize your potential?

You weren't born tired. Were you made this way, created tired by the hand of God? Nonsense!

Nature created the human body to stand great stress. God endowed all of us on a generous plan, as the late Dr. Samuel J. Meltzer once pointed out, shortly after the turn of the century, to an audience of physicians.

We have such a super-abundance of tissue in our bodies, Dr. Meltzer explained, that two-thirds of both kidneys may be removed "without serious determent"; normal breathing can be carried on though a great part of our lungs be destroyed; removal of one ovary or one testicle does not interfere in the slightest degree with their functions.

The thyroid gland possesses four or five times the amount of tissue necessary for the complete maintenance of health and life. We possess ten times as much of the vital substance manufactured by our adrenal glands as is necessary.

We usually have about twice as much blood sugar as we normally need for energy purposes. Dr. Walter B. Cannon tells us in *The Wisdom of the Body* (New York: W. W. Norton & Company, Inc., 1932, revised and enlarged 1939, p. 232) that although blood sugar is usually kept up to 0.09 or 0.10 per cent, it would have to fall to a level of 0.05 per cent to make serious trouble for us.

The invisible sentinel, the unconscious mind, keeps the blood sugar normally at a level twice as high as it needs to be for what Dr. Cannon calls "the threshold of adequate supply."

Other medical authorities point out that Nature supplies us with some organs, like the heart and diaphragm, with potential energies far beyond normal needs.

We are built to endure more than normal stress. An engineer planning a bridge designs it so that it will stand up under more than the maximum stress to which it will be subjected.

Who then will dare say that the greatest of all engineers designed our bodies so that they have barely enough of the *élan vital* to serve our needs during one short lifetime?

The "fearsome hand" that arranged our symmetry so that we can, if necessary, get along on less than half of our normal bodily equipment, must have given us enough energy to meet any situation likely to arise. What we have to do is learn to *use* the energy we have within us.

We can paraphrase the Psalmist who wrote: "This is the Lord's doing; it is marvelous in our eyes. This is the day which the Lord hath made; we will rejoice and be glad in it."

Let's think: "This is the body which the Lord hath made. It is marvelous in our eyes; and it abounds with energy. We will rejoice and be glad in it."

The body is the temple of the spirit; and to make it a temple fit for rejoicing, prayer, and other worth-while activities, it is gifted with an almost indescribable amount of potential energy at birth.

Who then is robbing us of our energy? If you are lacking in energy today, you yourself are the thief. Within your mind or body lurks the enemy. If you are chronically tired, something is physically or emotionally wrong. In this book, I hope to help you find what is wrong. Then remedy it, so that you can come into your very rich birthright of overflowing energy.

Why we get tired. If you are chronically tired, four chances out of five, the cause is spiritual or emotional. About 13 years ago, a New England doctor, F. N. Allan, made a careful study of 300 cases of fatigue. He found that nervous conditions were responsible for four out of five of those cases where the chief complaint was "that tired feeling." In only one case out of five were there definite physical disorders.

If you're much more tired than you should be, there's only one chance out of five that the cause is physical. Nevertheless, you dare not overlook the long shot.

If you're the one patient in five who has something physically wrong with him, you may need medical help in addition to a change in your attitudes. That's why Dr. Peter J. Steincrohn, M.D., says in *Live Longer and Enjoy It* (Englewood Cliffs, N. J.: Prentice-Hall, Inc., 1956): "Better take inventory if the juice of life has turned sour."

Do you value your body as much as your Cadillac? Once a year, if you value your health and respect your body as much as you respect your Ford, Dodge or Cadillac, you must have a physical examination.

If you don't have a regular physician you can trust, ask your county medical association for the name of a respected medico in your neighborhood. Don't put off that physical examination.

Only your doctor can detect whether there is a physical cause for your complaint. If you really have "tired blood," as the ads put it, your doctor can prescribe something that will do you a lot more good than the kind of medicine handed out at drug counters to all comers.

It might be anemia. Dr. Steincrohn tells of the 50-year-old businessman who came to him tense and jittery, complaining of weariness and of vague aches and pains. His blood test revealed that his blood cell count was a million red blood cells below par. He'd been overworking, under-eating, and under-sleeping.

Proper diet and rest quickly restored him to health and vibrant aliveness. Yes, he did need some iron therapy, but he needed it in the exact quantity prescribed by his doctor, and not necessarily the amount stated on the label of a patent medicine bottle.

However, even if your trouble is physical, it may not be caused by anemia or "tired blood."

A chest X-ray may reveal the cause. John, who in his twenties had been an athlete full of vigor and vitality, grew listless; dragged himself through endless days; couldn't understand why it was an effort to handle the simplest job.

If he'd taken "iron deficiency" medication, such as is frequently advertised for "tired blood," it wouldn't have helped. For a chest X-ray showed that John was in the very early stages of TB. At that stage, TB, properly treated, is easily arrested. Because John immediately put himself under the care of his physician, his lungs healed quickly. With recovered health, he gained renewed energy.

Then there was D——, a patient described by Dr. Steincrohn. He told his doctor that he felt he had been "born tired."

Your thyroid, the gland of destiny. A basal metabolism test showed that he was suffering from an underactive thyroid. Weighing less than an ounce, this butterfly-shaped gland in the neck can influence the whole course of your life. The product of the thyroid gland is indispensable to pep. Says Dr. Steincrohn: "If your thyroid has disrupted your normal 'energy production' by rioting or going on a sit-down strike, then modern medicine can promise miraculous cures. . . . The level on which you live often depends upon the efficiency of your thyroid gland" (*Live Longer and Enjoy it:* pp. 38–39).

A recent study by the School of Medicine at the University of Southern California indicated that one million middle-aged Americans are suffering from unsuspected lack of thyroid, causing them to be chronically tired. In a group of routine physical examinations of men working for large companies in Los Angeles, it was discovered that 12 per cent were suffering from curable, previously undetected lack of thyroid. Three-quarters of them were supervisors, who undoubtedly thought that it was the strain of their work that made them so tired. They were amazed to discover that their thyroid glands were largely to blame.

Don't jump to conclusions. You can't afford to jump to the conclusion that your thyroid gland is the mischief maker in your case. Maybe it is; maybe it isn't. Don't decide for yourself, but let your physician decide. Dr. Steincrohn warns; "When you take thyroid pills on your own you fondle dynamite!"

A thorough physical examination, by locating the real reason for your tired feeling, may transform you from a weak, listless person into one filled with drive and energy.

You owe your body at least the same amount of care you would give your car. If your car stalled several times a day; if its engine, instead of purring, pounded; if you were never sure it would take you where you wanted to go, wouldn't you bring it into a service station for a check-up?

If you put yourself in the hands of a competent physician, the result may very well be the tuning up of your motor to such an extent that you'll have power beyond anything you ever dreamed about.

If the cause of your weariness is physical, your doctor can prescribe medicines that will help you. If the cause is not physical, this book will tell you how to cope with those emotional factors that cause fatigue and lack of energy.

Yours is the body and the spirit which the Lord hath made. If they are marvelous in your eyes—and they should be—why not rejoice? If you do not consider them marvelous, you may change your mind when you have come with me on a journey of exploration of your great hidden potentials.

CHAPTER 1 IN A NUTSHELL

Nature has endowed all of us with more energy than we need to endure all the stresses and strains of a lifetime.

If, in spite of this generous allotment of energy, you find yourself tiring easily, you yourself are the enemy. You may be robbing yourself of energy by internal conflicts or by sheer carelessness, by giving your body less care than you give your car.

Four chances out of five, the cause of your trouble is emotional. But before you examine your emotional problems, see your doctor and have a thorough physical examination.

Aside from keeping physically fit, try to practice a certain rhythm in your life. In all curves of activity, you will find your energy rising from a warmup or a beginning to a climax. After the climax, always take at least a brief rest period. For the rhythm of life consists of a beginning, middle, climax, release from nervous tension, and rest.

2

Six Ways to Build Up Energy by Optimistic Thinking

*A*RE YOU LOOKING FORWARD TO TODAY?

If you are, you are building up a mysterious but very effective source of energy.

You're stretching that spring. Remember, Raymond C. Baird, the vibration engineer I mentioned in Chapter 1, says—when you stretch that spring, you can't help but build up energy.

So let's see what methods we can find for stretching that spring.

We'll assume that you've been to your doctor and have found that there is nothing seriously wrong with you physically. But still, day after day, you come home strangely tired.

You have within you a mysterious source of energy. Dr. Jay B. Nash, at that time Chairman of the Department of Physical Education, Health and Recreation at New York University, used to tell his students: "All of us are familiar with the phenomenon of the tired businessman who can barely wait to get home to rest at the end of the day. 'I'm all beat up,' he says. 'As soon as I get home, I'm going to take a hot bath, get into bed, and sleep around the clock.'

"Suddenly the phone rings. His best girl is on the line.

18

She tells him about a wonderful dance she'd like him to take her to. A vision of the fun he'll have comes rushing across his mind.

" 'Great,' he says. 'I'll pick you up at eight!'

"He leaves his office singing, bubbling over with energy.

"Where did that energy come from? If we knew its secret source, we'd be able to make a fortune, bottling it or putting it up in packages."

The source of that energy can't, in the present state of science, be bottled. But you can acquire it for yourself.

HOW YOU CAN DRAW UPON THIS SOURCE OF ENERGY

1. Regularly plan activities

It may be a pleasant trip, a social meeting of some organization to which you belong, or a party at your own home to which you invite only individuals whom you enjoy being with.

If you can plan two or three such evenings a week, so much the better.

About once a month, if possible, plan a short week-end trip. It should be to a place sufficiently close to your home so that the drive will not exhaust you.

Keep a record of things to do and places to go to. Then, when you have a free week-end, do one of those things, or go to one of those places.

Belong to one, two, or three clubs that interest you. This may lead to more invitations than you can always accept. From these, you can easily choose those that interest you most, that will give you occasions to look forward to.

Irwin Zucker, the public relations representative who has successfully helped to promote many Prentice-Hall books, once pointed out to me: "Individuals can gain a great deal by taking advantage of the social occasions arranged by their clubs. The social directors of these organizations often scout around to find places where their members can meet and spend enjoyable afternoons and evenings, at relatively little expense."

Personally I belong to four professional organizations that frequently plan outstanding social gatherings: the Greater Los Angeles Press Club, the Hollywood Women's Press Club, the California Association of Press Women, and the Hollywood Foreign Press Association.

A pleasant week in my life.   Let's take a recent week in my life.   On Saturday afternoon, my husband and I attended the Golden Flame banquet given by the California Association of Press Women.   On Sunday night we entertained four guests at our home, with my husband barbecuing the steaks while I made the salad and cooked the vegetables.   On Monday night we visited my family in a nearby suburb.   (His family is in the East).   On Tuesday night he didn't feel like going out, so I went with a friend to a movie preview of a soon-to-be released film.   On Wednesday night I attended a class in personality improvement given by one of Los Angeles' foremost teachers of this subject.   On Thursday night my husband and I saw another film previewed.   On Friday we spent a relaxing evening at home.

Such a program might seem a bit crowded for some tastes. But I find that meeting congenial friends for lunch or dinner or at a home party doesn't subtract from my energy; it leaves me glowing with happiness and energy.   My most active, energetic, and successful friends belong to professional groups. The more they do, within reasonable limits, the more energetic they become.

Personally, I keep "stay up late" parties to a minimum.   Our guests are extremely well trained.   Usually our parties break up before midnight.

One's social life must be planned so that it adds spice to one's existence without unduly draining energy.   So far as possible, our friends should be chosen from cheerful, positive-thinking individuals who look at life as a wonderful adventure and challenge.

2. Expect success, not failure

When most businessmen go into a venture, they do so realizing it is possible to make mistakes.   In fact, H. W. Miller, vice-president of IBM, recently said, "We're lucky if we're right four times out of five."

"A man would really enjoy looking at himself in the mirror every time he shaves if he could be right that often," another big executive told me.

Men like this are fully aware of the fact that on the road to success, you may encounter temporary failure. But they learn from their mistakes, leave them behind, and press forward.

Expecting success doesn't mean that you expect to be right five times out of five. It merely means that you think the odds are in your favor in a big venture—and that you *act* as if success is going to be the outcome of your endeavors.

Of course, before you start anything, you look into the facts carefully, never allowing yourself to be stampeded by the fellow who promises to double your money in two months if you act immediately.

Once you have carefully examined the facts and acted on them, you have a right to expect success.

Self-suggestion has an almost hypnotic effect. It has been proven by actual experiment that the expectation of success contributes physical energy not available to anyone who expects failure.

A college professor once gave some students some ineffective pills (doctors call them placebos) and a pep talk. He suggested that the students, under the influence of the pills, would be able to keep their arms stretched out for over an hour without any difficulty.

Mesmerized by the power of suggestion, they were able to do just that. Another group of students, who were not given either the pills or the talk, could keep their arms stretched out for only a couple of minutes.

The power of hypnosis. Under hypnosis, frail women have held up heavy loads as if they were nothing, while strong men, under negative suggestion, could hardly lift a pin.

I have watched Emile Franchel, a California hypnotist, hypnotize a group of individuals so that they were unable to unlock their fingers, once they had clasped them together. As long as they were responding to the suggestion that they couldn't unlock them, they couldn't.

On another occasion, he hypnotized a young man who had never before done any artistic work into the belief that he could do a fairly skillful oil painting. Surprisingly, the young man succeeded in doing a competent job. I doubt if hypnosis could make anyone do anything for which he didn't possess a hidden potential; but under hypnosis individuals troubled by doubts about themselves sometimes forget their doubts long enough to realize a hidden talent.

Almost always, we have the energy to do what we believe we can do! The conviction that something is within our powers gives us the energy we need to start doing it.

By giving you this magical conviction, hypnosis can temporarily draw on your hidden reserves of energy. For a more permanent effect, you need basic positive thinking. But that positive thinking should be realistic.

Robert M. Parks of Los Angeles, owner of the Robert M. Parks Co., specializing in electronic products, knew that he was gambling when he left his safe, secure job as vice-president of Shavex in order to launch his own company.

He knew he could fail, but he believed he would succeed. "Shavex," he told me, "had been absorbed by another electronics firm, but I was offered the right to retain my job as vice-president of Shavex, which was to become a subsidiary of a New York City holding company. In order to retain my job, I would have had to go to New York.

"I had always had an inner urge to build something of my own, so I decided in favor of starting my own business.

"I estimated the cost of getting into the business—about $25,000.

"Actually I knew that I could fail—every businessman knows that—but I believed that with my background of experience in electronics, I was much more likely to succeed."

So he acted as if final success was inevitable. First, he contacted the shaver shops. Their response was favorable and overwhelming.

He started off with two products, both of them accessories

that could be used so that a man could shave in his car. One accessory, the more novel one, can operate on the battery of the car.

This novel idea was the invention of a Hungarian named Roman Nemac. Though his idea was good, he didn't know how to finance or sell it, and was happy to make an agreement with Mr. Parks, who assumed the responsibility for packaging the product and selling it. It may seem like a coincidence that just at the time when he needed an unusual idea, Mr. Parks met a man who had the right one for him. I do not pretend to explain it. But when you stretch your energy spring by thinking positively, wonderful things do happen to you!

3. Plan ahead and budget your time

A friend of mine is a public relations man who has about 20 important chores to do each day. When he did these tasks in a random order, he found himself depleted of his energy quite early in the afternoon. Heroically, he worked nights and also week-ends. Often, at the end of a day, he would discover that he just hadn't found the time to do one or two extremely important things. Then when he was tired and harassed, he would attempt to do the kind of job to which he should have brought a fresh, clear mind.

He talked matters over with his accountant, who pointed out that he often did routine jobs when his energy peak was highest, and creative jobs when his energy was at its lowest peak.

The accountant suggested that he reverse the procedure, planning his most creative jobs for those hours when he felt as fresh as a head of lettuce in the garden, before its leaves have been picked.

The public relations man followed his suggestion, and found that with correct planning, he could get all his important tasks done with comparative ease.

If a task is creative, it should be done in those hours when you feel at your very liveliest.

Do you know the scientific way to determine those hours? All you need to discover your own golden hours is an ordinary thermometer. Obviously you can't go around the office with a thermometer in your mouth, but on your free days, such as Saturday and Sunday, take your oral temperature every hour.

You will find that at certain times of the day it is somewhat higher than at other times. Assuming you are healthy and don't have a fever, you are at the peak of your energy when your temperature is highest. Many individuals have the same golden hours every day. If you will test your temperature hourly for two or three week-ends, you'll be able to find your own golden hours. Do your most challenging jobs during those hours.

Plan the next day a few hours before bedtime so it will go well.

Failing to plan your day ahead of time, you may use up three-quarters of your vital energy in the hours when it is at its peak on matters that are not at all vital. Wouldn't you be foolish, knowing that your peak hours are from 10 A.M. to 12 P.M., to use those hours sharpening pencils, reading newspapers for entertainment, pasting stamps on envelopes? By planning your day ahead of time, you can devote your peak energies to the most important and challenging tasks that confront you.

My own peak energy is from 10 A.M. to 12:30 P.M. Whenever possible I use these hours to do what I consider my most creative writing. I can wash dishes, pull weeds, read, study, and interview celebrities for magazine articles at *other* hours. Of course, if a celebrity will see me only during one of my "golden" hours, I agree to such an appointment. But when given the privilege of choosing my own time for interviews, I usually select the late hours of the afternoon. My energy then is high enough to keep me mentally alert during the interview, but it is not at its absolute peak.

4. Start each day with a positive thought

The idea of positive thinking is so enchanting that it must be admitted that some of us become fanatical about its power. There is some slight danger in believing that one can remain at a peak level of positive thinking every hour of every day.

Just as we can't be perfect in anything else, we can't be perfect in this respect.

The curve for positive thinking might be compared to the curve we are trying to establish for prosperity. No rational businessman believes that the curve of prosperity will keep on mounting every month, with never a single dip. What our biggest businessmen hope for is that after we have reached a sharp peak, we can ride a little below that, and never again have such a shattering crevice of despair as hit us in the depression period.

You will have ups and downs in your thinking. Do not expect to feel as if you were sitting on top of the world all the time. Try to achieve a generally happy philosophy; find a quotation that helps you, and remind yourself of it at every possible opportunity.

Mrs. Alfred N. Steele, widow of the late Pepsi-Cola executive, (famous in her own right as Joan Crawford) faithfully reads the 23rd Psalm each morning. The words of the psalm fill her mind with the conviction that God, her Shepherd, will guide her through the day.

So potent are the words of this psalm that recently the newspapers told how Mrs. Wilma White, lost for six days in a desert wilderness in Texas, kept her courage up by repeating over and over to herself the words of the psalm. It gave her the strength to go on walking for hours through the wilderness, when normally she would have dropped with exhaustion.

It gave her faith enough to sleep and restore her energy, trusting to His protection. Without that faith, she couldn't have slept, surrounded as she probably was by wild animals and desert snakes.

Daytimes she repeated over and over to herself the words of the psalm:

"The Lord is my shepherd; I shall not want.
He maketh me to lie down in green pastures:
He leadeth me beside the still waters;
He restoreth my soul: He leadeth me in the paths of righteousness for his name's sake.

Yea, though I walk through the valley of the shadow of death,

I will fear no evil: for Thou art with me; Thy rod and Thy staff, they comfort me."

Positive thoughts over radio. If you listen to radio programs, don't limit your radio fare to disturbing news. Tune in at least once a day to a program that conveys positive thoughts.

No matter how busy you are, you should find some time during the day to listen to a program that gives you a feeling of spiritual or emotional uplift. In Dallas, Texas, Clinton William Murchison, owner of companies worth over 300 million dollars, listens each morning to Reverend Hawkins over KRLD, because, he says, the good Reverend strengthens his faith in the goodness of human nature.

This positive habit of thought enables him to face the greatest business risks calmly. He gets up very early in the morning because he is full of zest then, and wants to get his creative work done early.

Wherever you live, there is undoubtedly some local or national radio or TV program that carries the kind of message you should be listening to. Keep dialing your car or home radio till you find a program that presents a constructive, positive viewpoint.

Powerful positive thoughts produce power. The way in which positive thoughts actually produce physical energy is well-illustrated in a story Dr. Norman Vincent Peale tells in *The Power of Positive Thinking* (Englewood Cliffs, N. J.: Prentice-Hall, Inc., 1952).

Frank Hiller, a major-league baseball pitcher, he tells us, once pitched a game when the temperature was over 100 degrees. In the middle of the game, his energy sagged. But instead of allowing himself to be defeated by the thought that he couldn't possibly complete the game under these circumstances, Mr. Hiller repeated to himself this passage from the Old Testament: "But they that wait upon the Lord shall renew their strength; they shall mount up with wings as eagles; they shall run, and not be weary; and they shall walk, and not faint."

No doubt Frank Hiller had memorized this passage because it had previously served to renew flagging strength. Now as he repeated it to himself, he found his energy mounting, so that he completed the game with the feeling that he had a great deal of energy still in reserve.

His explanation to Dr. Peale was: "I passed a powerful energy-producing thought through my mind."

Yes, thoughts do produce energy. And thoughts can also rob you of energy. You cannot always choose what will happen to you, but you can choose the thoughts you will think, as you react to the happenings of the day.

Don't suggest negative thoughts to yourself. Haven't you known the kind of individuals who, when anything inconvenient happens to them, say, "Isn't that just my luck!" They are impressing themselves and everyone around them with the thought that they attract bad luck.

I know a woman who has had some fortunate things happen to her, and also some unfortunate things. She has never dwelt mentally on the unhappy happenings. She says to her friends, "I'm one of the luckiest women in the world. Go ahead— touch me for luck."

They do. She had several unfortunate marriages; she had wanted children and couldn't have them; she had lost the baby she hoped was coming to bless her life.

Mentally she put all these happenings behind her. With tremendous energy, she went into business for herself and created a fantastically successful company. She fell in love with a prominent, successful man, and finally achieved a happy marriage. Since she couldn't have children, she and her husband adopted a couple of lively youngsters.

Today she has every reason for being radiantly happy. But in the days when she could have succumbed to self-pity, she told her friends, "Touch me for luck." And she wasn't kidding.

Don't consider yourself a Jonah. Jonah's aren't popular. They never have been. When something seemingly unfortunate happens, remember that in the long run, it may turn out to be the best thing that ever happened to you. So don't waste energy weeping about your ill fortune.

There have been times when my husband has lost a job he valued. At such times, we have always said, "Who can tell whether this is good or bad luck, until more time has passed? Perhaps, as a result of this, we may find ourselves in a better spot than ever before."

A quotation my husband uses that always helps me is, "When one door closes, another door will open if you have done your best."

After I had handled a series called "The Role I Liked Best" for the *Saturday Evening Post* for about 12 years, the Post decided that we had covered most of the big stars and featured players, and that there was no longer any need for further articles for the series.

Inspired by my husband's philosophy, I asked myself, "What door will open next?"

In the meantime, I suggested a number of ideas to various magazines, and got several assignments. But for a time nothing I was doing gave me the satisfaction I had derived from handling the Post series.

Then *Your Life* decided to reprint an article I had once sold them on how to make decisions. As a result of that article and the blurb that accompanied it, I received a letter from Prentice-Hall, Inc., asking if I had any ideas for a self-help book. I suggested several ideas, finally coming up with the subject of my first non-fiction book, *You're Better Than You Think* (Englewood Cliffs, N. J.: Prentice-Hall, Inc., 1957).

Possibly the reprint in *Your Life* was pure happenstance. But I was able to go through the months with equanimity, because of the positive thought my husband gave me: "When one door closes, another will open." I knew that a door into work I would love would open to me.

Taking a positive attitude can be a turning point in your life. Ray Baird says the turning point in his life came after he had carried the torch for an idea for four years. As an engineer with The Fluor Corporation he had conceived a solution to the severe vibration of the Pipeline Suspension Bridge at Blythe, California. The problem had been to find out what was causing it. He had found that the wind was doing it. To solve this, it would be necessary to put little fin-shaped aluminum wings on the bridge.

But no one would buy his solution.

"It seemed too simple, though it was fundamental," he said.

For about four years he could get no one to do anything about it.

"No matter how right you are," he says today, "you're wrong, if you're not sure you're right."

You have to be sure enough to persuade someone else to back you.

The turning point came when he got enough poise and self-assurance to walk into the office of Clyde Blohm, at that time his boss, and to say, "Give me the authority to settle this once and for all. Let's build a wind tunnel, and make a model to prove my theory."

He spoke with such assurance that Clyde Blohm said, "All right."

Ray Baird's theory worked like a charm on the model. Then Fluor called in the chief engineers for the gas companies. The model helped sell them. His solution worked not only on the model, but also on the Pipeline Suspension Bridge. It helped make Ray Baird famous.

"A friend of mine," says Mr. Baird, "says that the difference between success and failure lies in positive action. In this instance, it hinged on my deciding one day, 'I myself must do what I can to change this discouraging situation,' then walking 15 feet into the office of my boss, and saying, 'Give me the authority to settle this once and for all.'" That one moment of positive action abruptly altered Ray Baird's entire career.

5. Maintain a serene attitude

If you knew how worried I used to be over every big and little problem that arose in my life 17 or 18 years ago, you'd say: "Look who's talking."

Sometimes I feel as if I have almost nothing in common with

the woman I was then. She was a woman who wept inwardly
over everything, became distraught if a single person criticized her, found it hard to get along with her family, often got
into arguments with her own mother. She was married, but
she was in a fog about her own husband. She didn't know
whether or not her marriage was a mistake.

"Was that woman I?" I ask myself sometimes, disbelievingly.

My mother and I haven't had an argument in years. When
someone criticizes me unfavorably, I feel slightly hurt, but get
over it quickly. I know that some critics criticize out of envy,
others out of malice, still others because of their own deep in-
feriority feelings. If a criticism is warranted, I accept it, and
try to improve myself if I can.

I am still married to the same husband. But he doesn't
seem like the same man to me, because I'm not the same
woman.

When one of us is temporarily angry about something, we
blow off a little steam; then kiss and make up within ten minutes. We never waste enough energy on quarrels to interfere
with our pleasant frame of mind. On the other hand, we don't
suppress our opinions about things that are important to us,
and in that way build up resentments that would also sap
energy.

How did I, a woman who was a bunch of nervous tensions,
achieve an attitude and atmosphere of serenity?

First of all, I learned to make up my own mind about important things, and not to accept the opinions or valuations
of others, simply because they were forceful in expressing them.

When I began to respect my own judgment, others began to
respect it, too.

The big secret is to find out what is really important to you,
and hold on to that, even when everything else in your world
goes to pieces. You have to ask yourself: "What is really most
important in my life? Money? Being thought of fondly by
the individuals with whom I deal? Having self-respect?
Love and marriage? Children?"

Examine the things you consider important, and see if they

really are. For instance, suppose you have been rejected by a
club you hoped to join. You wanted very much to be a part
of that group. But for some reason, they decided you didn't
fit in. Is it really so important to belong to that particular
group, or may you discover in time that there are other groups
you'll find more congenial?

*A sense of perspective is extremely important to your mental
poise.* When you have reached the age of reason, it is *your*
sense of perspective that should matter most to you, not that
of your mother, father, brother or sister. In a family constella-
tion there is usually one member who tries to dominate the
others; but if you are wise, you will listen to what that member
says, then act according to your own sense of perspective.
For instance, you may have a brother who believes it's silly
to marry unless the marriage is socially advantageous. Let
him live by his viewpoint, if he wishes. Why should you?
You can have your own.

Weeping over trifles will wear out your friends. Of course,
if you face real grief, they will respect your sorrow. The person who tries to be stoical in the face of a real tragedy is asking too much of his body.

A beautiful widow who had lost her husband said to one of
her friends, "I know that I must control myself. I know I
mustn't cry."

The friend who was a doctor said, "Why not? Why
shouldn't you cry? Under circumstances like these, tears were
given us by God because of their healing power. They are a
safety valve, not something to be ashamed of."

None of us admires the man or woman (usually it's a
woman) who resorts to tears on slight provocation. Such
women, Dr. Alfred Adler once said, try to run their homes and
their husbands through water power.

Such women exhaust not only themselves but everyone
around them.

Learn to use words correctly. Would you be surprised to
learn that the proper use of the English language has a great
deal to do with maintaining one's mental poise? A man who

had lost a great deal of money in business said, "I'm ruined. This is a disaster. I can't possibly face this problem. This load is much too great for me to bear."

His adviser sat down with him, toted up his assets, and found that far from being ruined, it was possible for him to save the situation to a certain extent. He had lost a good deal of money. Is this disaster? Not if you really tote up your assets. The man had a good mind, a great deal of ability. The qualities that had built up one fortune for him were capable of building up another.

Someone once asked the late Mike Todd, "How many millions have you made and lost?" "Who counts?" he answered.

"I have been broke but never poor," he once said jauntily. "Being poor is a quality of spirit."

One of the most popular members of the Greater Los Angeles Press Club is Joe Riley, a jovial Irishman, who once said, "I realized long ago that I'd never have enough money to buy happiness. So I made up my mind that whatever happened, I'd find happiness another way—by building up friendships."

He considers himself a rich man, and among the thousands of members, not one is richer in friends than he. He keeps working, though he is in his sixties; he has arranged all sorts of affairs at the club, and he has found his happiness through friendships. His thoughts about himself are happy, buoyant thoughts.

Thoughts are obviously made of words or pictures. If you think along gloomy lines and use melodramatic words, you can convince yourself that losing your pet dog is a world-shaking tragedy.

Semantics—using the right word to express your thoughts—is a great study. If you'd like to know more about it, you might read *Word Power—Talk Your Way to Life Leadership* by Vernon Howard (Englewood Cliffs, N. J.: Prentice-Hall, Inc., 1958). When you find yourself inclined to use a negative, melodramatic word to express your problems, stop.

Try to think of yourself objectively, as if you were somebody else. If Mr. Jones came to you and told you that he was facing bankruptcy, would you think for one second that he was "ruined," "disgraced," and that he might as well kill himself?

If you are Mr. Jones, such thoughts may come to you.

Actually a human being rarely faces bankruptcy. Temporary financial bankruptcy, possibly. Temporary panic or grief, yes. But we are so extraordinary, God has made human beings so terrific, that it is almost impossible to bankrupt an individual morally or spiritually. "For God hath not given us the spirit of fear; but of power, and of love, and of a sound mind."

Keep calm. You are strong and brave enough to face anything that can possibly happen to you. If you aren't sure of this, pray for strength, and your prayers will be answered.

6. Learn to think independently

Haven't you known individuals who just couldn't make up their minds? Before taking any step, they'd consult at least two dozen acquaintances. Not all of those consulted knew all the circumstances. Consequently, they sometimes gave advice that was uninformed, biased, and occasionally stupid.

A woman whose husband had deserted her and asked for a divorce told an acquaintance that she was unhappy and thinking of asking for a divorce. The acquaintance gave her a long dissertation on the horrors of divorce and said that most children born to couples who got divorces later became juvenile delinquents (a very exaggerated statistic).

This threw her into a further panic. She shouldn't have confided her problems to such a casual acquaintance. But as long as she was talking about her problems she should have leveled about them. If you present your problem dishonestly, you'll naturally get an answer that is not at all helpful.

You can also tear your energy to shreds by consulting too many people about your problems. One says "yes," the next says "no," the third says "maybe." Influenced by each in turn, you start to do something, then change your mind, reverse your direction.

There are times, of course, when experts must be consulted:

lawyers for legal problems, doctors for medical ones, and so on. But most of the time, for the most important decisions of your life, you must depend on yourself.

Form the habit of making minor decisions quickly. You don't have to waste three hours on the 10-cent problem of whether to wear a blue or a gray tie with a certain suit.

When it comes to important decisions, get the facts first; write down the alternative solutions, and their possible consequences.

Get a sheet of paper, and write down the reasons for and against each decision. Give each reason a certain number, from one to ten, depending on the importance of that reason to you.

See how the alternatives look numerically.

Then pray for wisdom, and sleep on the problem.

Once you have made your decision, act on it. The sooner you act, the more energy you will have not only in tackling this problem, but all the other problems in your life.

One important unsolved problem can throw you into a tizzy that will render you unable to work, sleep, or eat.

So find the best solution you can as quickly as you can and act. Nothing is more negative than fretting and stewing. Nothing is more positive than action. If you have difficulty making decisions, compel yourself to make one decision a day.

Remember how Hamlet destroyed his energy and almost destroyed his life because he couldn't make up his mind? You don't have to be like that. You can start right now, this very instant, forming the habit of making sensible decisions, based on your own good judgment. This will free for you more energy than you ever dreamed of.

YOUR SIX WAYS TO BUILD UP ENERGY BY OPTIMISTIC THINKING

1. *Every week plan at least one activity you'll look forward to.*

2. *Expect success, not failure.*

3. *Plan ahead and budget your time to avoid tensions and confusion.   Find out what your peak hours are, and plan your most important and demanding tasks for those hours when your energy is highest.*

4. *Read, memorize or listen to some positive thoughts each day.   Start each day with a positive thought.*

5. *Maintain a serene attitude toward problems in life.*

6. *Learn to think independently, and to make your own decisions.*

3

How Never to Be Bored

VERY OFTEN, WHEN YOU THINK YOU'RE TIRED, YOU'RE REALLY
bored. Boredom can make you feel listless, apathetic, and
even cause you to do work that is far below your standards.

Your work may suffer if you are bored. Once a group of
college students in a German university were asked to draw a
series of vertical lines, following a certain pattern, on some
sheets of paper. They were warned not to stop until they received permission to do so.

As they drew, they grew more and more bored with the
whole experiment, and their lines became less and less like the
original pattern. The quality of the work deteriorated badly.

However, the moment they were told to finish the page on
which they were then working, the quality of the work took a
sudden spurt. The lines were then drawn just as carefully as
they had been at the beginning.

If it hadn't been for that end spurt, anyone, seeing the
deterioration of the work, would have said that the students
were fatigued almost beyond endurance.

But were they? If they were, how could they, when told
that the work was nearing an end, suddenly turn out beautifully drawn patterns again?

Obviously, they were not really tired, just bored.

Many people are only half alive much of the time. Now
what has this to do with you and me? We often feel ex-

hausted for the same reason: boredom. Experts have estimated that the average man spends about a third of his active
life being bored. Just imagine that. If you sleep eight hours,
you may be spending one third of your waking life—more than
five hours—in a state where you are only half alive.

Would you choose to be a Zombie? If someone told you
that for the rest of your life you would have to choose between
being a vital human being and a Zombie, what choice would
you make?

Who on earth, given the choice, would choose to be a living
corpse, when instead he could be full of energy?

Why some people become Zombies. No one facing this
choice on a conscious level would choose to be a Zombie.
And yet, so strange are the forces influencing human behavior
that a large percentage of those you know have unconsciously
chosen the road to Zombieism.

Why?

One reason may be that in some sections of our civilized
countries it's thought smart to be blasé. The jaded person may
kid himself that he's superior. Smugly he smiles at the tastes
of the average person. By taking the attitude that he's difficult to please, he fools himself into believing that he has a
superior mind.

But even if his mind were superior, he would still be neuro-
tically inferior to those who live with a boiler full of steam.

Of course, the jaded, pseudo-sophisticated man isn't the
only Zombie in our culture.

Anyone can, by limiting his interests and narrowing his way
of life, turn himself into a Zombie.

Enthusiasm for life pours energy into your body. When
you're full of enthusiasm, your glands pour into your blood
stream hormones that fill you with energy. But accept a dull,
listless attitude, cut yourself down to one or two interests, and
your hormones say, "Well, there's no use working overtime for
this guy. He doesn't need any energy. He doesn't even
know what to do with the little energy he's already getting
from us."

If you want abundant energy, you must stir up your interest in life and its many extraordinary manifestations.

Keats and you. There must be times when like the great poet Keats you feel

> Like some watcher of the skies
> When a new planet swims into his ken:
> Or like stout Cortez when with eagle eyes
> He stared at the Pacific and all his men
> Look'd at each other with a wild surmise
> Silent, upon a peak in Darien.

What made Keats feel that way? More important, how can you and I make ourselves feel that way? How can we change our slumbering, listless ordinary selves into men and women who are almost never bored? Psychologists say that there is probably no one who isn't bored during some section of the day, but we can certainly achieve a state of mind where the moments of boredom are so few and far between that we hardly know they exist.

I'm hardly ever bored. Even if it sounds boastful, I must admit that I am one of those individuals who rarely know what it means to be bored. Sometimes others, envying my freedom as a free-lance writer who interviews famous men and women, say, "Well, I certainly would find life exciting, too, if I could interview the kind of celebrities you frequently meet."

Be interested and you will find all life around you interesting. Actually, I sometimes find John Doe, who happens to be sitting in the restaurant in the seat next to mine, and Mrs. John Doe in the next seat on the bus just as exciting, in their own way, as Bette Davis in her way, or Art Linkletter in his. Unless you talk to your next-door neighbor, you will never find out what makes him tick. A woman who always complained that she didn't know any interesting people discovered, after two of her neighbors had moved away, that one of them was a great physicist at a university, the other a social service worker at a county hospital. It was her own fault that she had never taken the trouble to know them better. She had assumed, without actually speaking to them, that they were colorless.

I am fully convinced that if you find someone uninteresting, it may be because of some emptiness in you that fails to respond to him. Surely God never created a really dull human being.

SIX WAYS TO ESCAPE BEING BORED

To keep from being bored, I have found six simple rules very helpful.

1. Listen to everyone you meet

Frankly, I don't listen to others simply because Dale Carnegie advised it was a method of winning friends. Listening to people is fun! I do it for purely selfish reasons. There is always the possibility that while listening to someone, I may feel as Keats did when he read a certain book: "like some watcher of the skies
When a new planet swims into his ken."

To me all the men and women I meet, from the humblest to the most important, are more exciting than planets. Who can tell, at first meeting, what new discoveries one will make about a man, the most thrilling of all earth's creatures? Whenever I meet anyone new, I ask myself: What is he like? What things excite him? What does he believe in? How does he handle other men and women?

You, too, can have fun collecting people. When you first meet someone, how can you tell in advance what adventures in friendship you are going to have? Who can tell what strange facts you may learn, what inspiring meeting of the minds is going to take place?

The first time I met my husband, we were on a Yosian hike in New York. On that first hike, I was stung by a bee, and the exciting adventure that day was his simple kindness in applying a poultice of mud to my face.

We have now been married for 20 years, and I find that we are still making discoveries about each other.

Still, when I talk of collecting people, I am not speaking just of romance. Every meeting with another individual can be high adventure.

When you listen to others and draw them out, your whole life is enriched by it.

The woman who brought her eyebrows home for approval. One of the most hilarious evenings of my life was spent with a group of classmates who were taking a course in personality development at the Sheraton Town House in Los Angeles. Afterwards about eight of us decided to have coffee and dessert in the Zebra Room of the Town House.

We discussed the course, current fashions, and the make-up expert who had visited our class. We all had lively opinions, and the good-natured banter flew back and forth across the table.

But to me the highlight of the evening was the discovery of a charming young married woman named Lee. She had had a conference with the make-up expert, who said her eyebrows should be higher, and who had proceeded to draw a higher eyebrow on one side of her face.

Then the expert wanted to do the same thing to the other side.

"No," said Lee firmly. "I want to bring both eyebrows home to my husband, and see which one he likes better."

Chortling about it, she said, "I'm sure the make-up expert must think I'm completely mad. However, I'm an individualist, and I won't change my eyebrows on anyone's advice, unless my husband agrees with that person."

I had to laugh at the idea of a woman bringing home her eyebrows to her husband for approval, just as if she were bringing home two dresses to choose from. And I said to myself, "I hope I get to know Lee better some time in the future." A madcap, individual sense of humor is delightful; and when we find that precious gift in someone, why not expose ourselves to it?

People are as exciting as planets. Let the astronomers have their planets. Let the bacteriologists have their wonderful discoveries about the small living creatures who threaten us at times, and help us at other times. Personally, I'll take the Lees and the John Does, and make new, interesting discoveries about my friends and acquaintances every day.

What has this to do with energy? When you're constantly interested in others, your glands work better; your whole body seems more in tune with the universe; life is never flat or dull. And you never feel flat or dull either.

2. Believe that you possess all the energy you need

William James once said, "Believe that you possess significant reserves of health, energy, and endurance and your belief will create the fact."

You have enough energy to do anything that interests you. The more intensely you become interested in something, the more abundantly will your glands supply you with the "plusses" of energy that enable you to feel 100 per cent alive most of the time.

Boredom drains energy from you; enthusiasm builds it up. Why do you suppose colleges use cheer leaders, wave pennants and flags in the air, and have student bands play exciting music at every big football game? Why do coaches give pep talks, in which they make the men feel that the whole future of the college depends on their "do or die" attitude?

So great is the energy created by such activities that when football players are examined after a game, significant quantities of sugar are found in their urine. According to Dr. Walter Cannon, their enthusiasm produces this increase in blood sugar, giving them more energy. Who ever heard of a successful football or baseball player without enthusiasm?

As for your great coaches, which of them could have achieved greatness without enthusiasm? They themselves *must* be enthusiastic in order to pass on this attitude to their teams.

The secret of a great coach. Pat O'Brien, who had the good fortune to meet Knute Rockne, once told me, "He had an indestructible spirit, and a wonderful faculty of renewing the

strength of his players—of giving them confidence, making
them feel they were the most unbeatable bunch that ever went
into a huddle."

The enthusiasm he transmitted to them gave them abundant
energy.

Energy is just as important to your success as it was to theirs.
Professor Lewis Terman, head of the Department of Psychology at Stanford, once said, "Intelligence alone is not the
whole thing in success. Moderate intelligence with high enthusiasm will often succeed where high intelligence with low
enthusiasm fails. Enthusiasm alone may turn failure into
success."

B. N. "Woody" Woodson, president of the American General
Life Insurance Company of Houston, Texas, has said, "The
man who will never lift his temperature to the boiling point
will never achieve anything worth-while in this world; the
man who can and will keep his boiler at full-steam by keeping
the fire of enthusiasm at white heat, can achieve anything in
this world to which he may reasonably aspire."

How exactly are you going to lift your enthusiasm to the
boiling point?

Shakespeare, who knew so much about the human heart,
said, "Assume a virtue, if you have it not."

So the first step in building enthusiasm for anything is to
act as if you were already enthusiastic.

From William James we have learned that assuming an attitude can easily lead to the real emotion. He believed that
we don't smile because we're happy, but are happy because
we smile. He says that "we feel sorry because we cry, angry
because we strike, afraid because we tremble."

He might have added that we feel enthusiastic because we
act as if our batteries were super-charged.

So act enthusiastic, even if you don't feel enthusiastic. If
you act out an emotion, a tide of real feeling will eventually
engulf you.

One of the fathers in my community became convinced that

he ought to play a more active part in the local PTA meetings.
He went to one, and was quite bored by the discussions.

He told himself sternly, "I must show some interest. If I
want to have any say about the way the schools in my community are run, I just can't sit here acting indifferent."

The moment someone suggested an idea that he half-way
liked, he jumped to his feet, and said, "That's a great idea.
Why don't we try it?"

Real enthusiasm can grow out of acting enthusiastic. For
two weeks he acted out an emotion he didn't really feel.
And then suddenly something strange happened. He found
himself growing enthusiastic. He began to care about the
parent teachers' association. He got to his feet and said
earnestly, "Why can't we have famous speakers on child psychology talk to our group on the problems our children face?"

He was made chairman of a committee to arrange for such
speakers. A new interest had entered his life, and with this
new interest, he found new energy.

That brings us to our second specific point on how to build
up enthusiasm. It's easy to be enthusiastic about a subject on
which you know a great deal. Whether the subject is collecting stamps or fishing for marlin, if you're genuinely interested,
you'll show enthusiasm.

But suppose you're a salesman, and one of your customers is
mad about fishing, an occupation you've never enjoyed.

You'd better do your best to become interested, or else go
after a different customer. Of course, it's perfectly possible
that your product is so fine, your service so good that your customer won't give a hang whether you can discuss marlin fishing intelligently or not. However, if there are equally good
products on the market, and you want this man to like you
well enough to order from you, you'd better read up on the
subjects that interest him.

This is particularly true of the salesmen dealing with foreign
countries. A certain salesman went to a town in South America, convinced that he could land a big order because he had

a good product, and was willing to sell at a reasonable price.

He knew nothing about his customer, about his customer's country, the poets of that country, its literature, and its heroes.

He thought he could swing the customer right into a discussion of the product. He couldn't. Instead the customer wanted to know his opinion of a certain poet, a certain sculptor, and the national hero. When the conversation revealed his abysmal ignorance of all these subjects, the man virtually threw him out of his office.

You should have enough hobbies, about which you can be enthusiastic, to build up your own energy. And you should have enough hobbies so that when you meet someone and he reveals his interest in some special subject, you're likely to know something about it, too. At least, you should have enough energy to listen intelligently. Oliver Wendell Holmes talked of the "white magic" of listening, and he was right. You are most likely to possess that white magic if you acquire a heartfelt interest in many subjects.

Everything you really *want* to do or learn gives you additional energy.

If your work bores you, you won't have much energy for it. What do you do? Either change to another field, or learn to like it.

How to acquire an interest in your job. Here is a man who has to sell shirts in a department store. Nothing could be more boring, he thinks.

Actually, the work doesn't have to be boring. He can learn something about how the shirts are made, how the different fabrics wear, whether one brand is really better than another.

Furthermore, he can take an interest in his customers. Why does this one step up to him with an air of authority and say: "I want such and such a shirt, in such and such a size," while another man hems and haws, and can't make up his mind whether he really wants a yellow shirt or a white one? How should he treat these men? He might try a couple of methods on each, to see how different types respond.

And he might, at his own counter, become a kind of Elmer Wheeler of the shirt world, practicing the art of sizzlemanship, which is simply the art of finding the right words to say to get the most favorable response.

A third way of building up enthusiasm is to look at the advantages of an assignment, a job, a vacation resort, or anything else that happens to fall to your lot. It is very easy to harp mentally on the disadvantages of a job or place, and get into such doldrums that you cease enjoying the situation. On the other hand, it is perfectly possible to kindle a fire under yourself by looking at the sunny side of any situation.

Recently, I was given an assignment on Shirley Temple's return to the entertainment world. The editor felt—and rightly—that a better article could be written by interviewing those who had known Shirley in the past than by interviewing merely the star herself.

Knowing that I would have to interview about a dozen people for a magazine that was moderately budgeted, I might have approached the assignment with little enthusiasm. There was a good chance that the check I would finally receive would not pay for the amount of time I'd have to invest.

But I began thinking of the advantages of this assignment. Working on it would be like working on a detective story, gathering all the facts I possibly could in the time at my disposal. I'd undoubtedly meet a good many interesting individuals.

I did. Each dropped a clue as to where I could get some more information. By the time I was through with my article, I'd had a thoroughly good time. Some of my enthusiasm must have shown in the final article, for the editor—bless her— not only praised it, but increased the amount of the check to make up for the extra work.

Actually, the article had been fun to do. The interviewing had been thoroughly enjoyable, because my enthusiasm gave me twice as much energy as I might have had otherwise.

3. Make sure that your job challenges your powers

The job that doesn't challenge all your powers will either bore or exasperate you. Nathan S. Massion of North Hollywood, California, was an extremely successful pharmacist.

But by nature he is a creative person, and after a certain period of working hard at his job, he felt as if he had had it. Obviously, preparing prescriptions gives little scope to the imagination. And Mr. Massion wanted to do something creative.

Years previously, he had given up a promising career as an artist because an eye doctor had warned him that he was ruining his eyes, and would have to find a career that would be easier on them.

The idea of helping to create a magazine appealed to him very much. To attempt such a job sounded risky, since it would be hard on the eyes, too. But so great was his need for doing creative work that he went to his eye doctor and said: "I'm going to do something that I know you'll consider foolish. I'm going to take a job as art director and assistant publisher of a magazine. Is there anything I can do to preserve my eyes, in spite of that kind of job?"

The eye doctor smiled.

"You were a young man when I warned you to give up art," he said. "Now your eyes will not deteriorate very much. If it means so much to you, go ahead and take the job. Just don't hold the sheets of paper, the layouts, and the newsprint too close to your eyes."

Today Mr. Massion is very happy in his job as assistant publisher and art director of the magazine, *"Western Grower and Shipper,"* devoted to the interests of vegetable growers. Rejoicing in the opportunity to use his creative powers in his work, he has energy to spare, not only for his work, but also for healthful recreation, and a very happy home life with his wife and two children.

4. Get fun out of activities with others

We renew ourselves by associating with others. We dry up and churn inside when we try to live for and by ourselves. Consequently, if you can find your fun in activities in which you're associated with others, you'll sometimes reap a double benefit. Every man, even a hermit, needs human contacts, or his mind will dry up and his energy wither.

Nine prisoners of science. Dr. Jules Masserman (a famous professor of psychiatry, who studied why cats sometimes go crazy) once reported on an experiment that almost drove a group of nine healthy young men mad. These men lay on beds in a soundproofed room, with goggles over their eyes devised so they could see nothing, and cardboard tubes over their hands so that they could touch nothing. Each of the young men had his own cubicle, so that there was no communication with the others. They left their tiny quarters only to eat or go to the bathroom. Each man was in a state of voluntary solitary imprisonment.

During the one and a half to six days that these men lay imprisoned in their voluntarily chosen cubicles, they began to experience hallucinations, and to hear strange voices. They were not only bored; they were also showing some of the first signs of insanity.

When they finally were restored to the mad world we all live in, with its multitude of problems, they were delighted. For they were being restored to a world in which they could communicate with others. They rapidly recovered their sanity and energy.

Actually, energy never vanishes, so what had happened in their cubicles was that their latent energy boiled within their minds, creating hallucinations.

One hundred per cent rest is rarely a solution for fatigue. These nine men had a terrific rest, but no fun. When all of our energy is directed inward and none of it outward into activity, we're headed for trouble. We must have fun to stay sane.

Naturally, each of us has a different conception of fun. You may love popular music; my husband may prefer an evening at the opera, and I may prefer the latest movie.

But be honest with yourself. Be sure that you *do* have fun at your self-chosen form of recreation. If your idea of fun is going into the woods and searching for trailing arbutus, by all means go there instead of to a beach party, which might bore you to death.

However, if you can find a band of enthusiastic arbutus
hunters, join them.   If you're a bird watcher, join a bird watch-
ers' group.   There is renewal of spirit in being with congenial
individuals who enjoy some of the same things you do.   And
when you are renewed in spirit, you are naturally more
energetic.

5. Keep your mind alive

"But I haven't time," you protest.   "Who has time to do all
that?"

You can spend half an hour a day reading.   You have.
Have you ever stopped to think how much reading you could
actually do if you devoted half an hour a day to it?   Sir William Osler, one of the great physicians and teachers of medical
students, made it an iron-clad rule to read 15 minutes each
evening before he retired.   As a result, he became an authority
not only on medical matters but also on some literary subjects.

Someone once estimated that if a man read 15 minutes a day
every day, he would become extremely well-read, since he
could read the equivalent of all the Harvard Classics.

Read when you have to wait for someone or something.
During the course of any day, there may be moments when
you feel fidgety waiting for a bus, a street car, an appointment
with your doctor, your dentist, or a prospective buyer.   Why
not carry with you a book or a pocket-size magazine that you
can delve into at such times?

Two men met one day while waiting for the same train.   It
was late, and one complained loudly about the railroad's inef-
ficiency.   Then he turned to the other man, who was quietly
reading a book he had brought with him.   "How can you sit
there reading?" he asked.   "Doesn't it infuriate you when a
train is late?"

The man with the book grinned.   "No," he smiled.   "I find
it much pleasanter to spend the time reading.   In that way, I
don't lose energy through boredom or nervous tension.   Both
of us will get to our destination at the same time, but I won't
be upset when we get there."   And with that, he went back to
his book.

Take an adult education course. For those who would rather study in a group than by themselves, the adult education schools, the junior colleges, and the colleges in their extension courses offer a variety of subjects to suit every taste.

Recently, Lee Halem, my youngest sister, decided that bringing up three charming young children was not enough to absorb all her energy, now that they were spending a good deal of their time in school. She got a job teaching the first grade. Not content with that alone, she also took several courses, including one on comparative religion.

Unwilling to shut himself away from that phase of her mental activities, her husband decided to take the course at the same time.

Listening to their many discussions on the religions of the world, I know perfectly well that here are two individuals who will never know the meaning of the word "boredom."

Comparative religion may not be your dish of tea at all. But somewhere in your town someone is giving a course that would stimulate you mentally. Why not take it? And if you honestly feel that you can't find the time for a complete course, at least try to attend one lecture a week in the field of your choice.

6. Join the do-it-yourself movement

Surely there is something you can learn to do yourself. It may be growing bigger and better tomatoes, or gladioli, or building your own fence. Perhaps you can learn to paint your own bedroom, build your own fireplace, or construct some built-in furniture.

There is something exhilarating about discovering that you can do things with your hands. That's why in the treatment of mental illness, occupational therapy is often used to help bring about recovery.

But you don't have to be ill to get joy out of using your hands.

Try to figure out some way to use them today. Decide on something you want to do with your hands and get started.

Don't even insist on that old cliché: "Anything worth doing is worth doing well."

You don't have to be tops at a hobby to enjoy it. Even if you're second rate, doing things with your hands will keep you alive and interested.

Going to a movie, a play, or the opera may be exciting. But nothing will give you as great a thrill as creating with your own two hands something born out of your mind.

The glow of creation. I have watched the glow of creation on my husband's face, as he created, out of a few pieces of metal and some sticks of wood, a television lamp we could use. And I remember the inspired look on the face of a young husband who proudly showed visitors the couch he had personally built, the bookcase he had painted himself, and the old student lamp he had picked up in a junkshop and shined to such brightness you couldn't tell it from a new lamp.

We are all creators. Since we are all made in God's image, we are all creators, like our own Creator. Each of us can create *something.* It doesn't have to be a sonnet or a great painting. It may be a little gadget that meets some need your wife has mentioned, like the aluminum no-burn stand my husband created for me when I confessed that my pots often burned when I wandered away to do something else, completely forgetting the boiling water in the pots.

Creators are never bored while actually creating. You and I—we're both creators. And what right has a creator ever to be bored? No right at all, and no reason.

If, right now, or at any time in the future, you begin to feel bored, try to think of something you can create. No man, caught in the thrill of creating something, has ever been known to be bored while at his task.

SIX WAYS OF BUILDING UP ENERGY
BY KNOCKING OUT BOREDOM

1. Listen to everyone you meet. Adopt an attitude of happy expectancy whenever you meet someone new.

2. *Believe that you possess all the energy you need to fill your life with sparkling interest. Act as if you have enthusiasm, and true enthusiasm will follow.*

3. *Make sure that your job challenges your powers, within reason. Don't settle for something you find easy but dull.*

4. *Associate with others in activities that you find are fun for you.*

5. *Keep your mind alive by reading or taking courses in subjects that interest you, or by going to lectures.*

6. *Join the do-it-yourself movement, and stimulate yourself by attempting some creative activity.*

4

How to Build Up the
Self-Confidence That Builds
Energy

*A*CCORDING TO A FAMOUS STORY, A WELL-KNOWN ARCHITECT
was once summoned as a witness in a court case. During the
course of his examination, one of the attorneys asked him:
"Will you please identify yourself for the court? What is your
occupation?"

Without blinking an eyelash, the architect gave his name,
then stated, "I am the finest architect in the world."

Later a friend remonstrated with him. "How could you say
a thing like that?" he asked. "Didn't you realize that such a
statement might lead people to believe that you are immodest?"

"I know," said the architect, "but I couldn't help myself.
After all, I was under oath."

THE IMPORTANCE OF SELF-CONFIDENCE

Many of us, chuckling over that story, feel that this architect
was overwhelmingly conceited. Nevertheless, there was considerable foundation for his conceit. He was internationally

acclaimed for his great work and his daring departures from tradition. His energy was also fabulous.

Would he have been so energetic if he had had less faith in himself?

It's perfectly true that such conceit, so openly expressed, may repel others. But it is also true that supreme self-confidence often propels the confident person the way ignited rocket fuel sends a guided missile into space.

We don't have to blow our own horns. We don't have to tell others how good we are. But we do have to act as if we were self-confident.

Nearly all great men are self-confident. The biographies of successful men prove that nearly all possessed or acquired the gift of self-confidence.

Each of them, of course, expresses that sense of his own worth differently. George Markidian, the famous San Franciscan restaurateur, said, "I have always believed in God, in this country, and in myself."

Without that triple faith, he wouldn't have had the courage to start a fine restaurant against the terrific competition that prevails in San Francisco.

A great singer, Mario Lanza, speaks frankly of his God-given voice. He knows it's a thrilling voice. But he doesn't try to take the complete credit for it himself. He knows his voice comes from a great Creative Power operating through him.

The legend that Lindbergh is extremely modest and never has believed in his own abilities was created by newspaper men for popular consumption. Of course Lindbergh believed in himself! Where else would he have gotten the courage to make that dangerous flight overseas?

From modesty? From humility? From great doubts about himself?

Humility in the great is not lack of self-confidence. As John Ruskin once said, "I believe that the first test of a really great man is his humility. I do not mean by humility doubt of his own power. But really great men have a curious feeling that the greatness is not in them but through them."

If you don't have sufficient confidence, you will often find yourself lacking in energy. For self-confidence ignites the fuel that propels your engine.

If you have to use half your energy battling yourself into doing something that you don't think will be a success, you have little energy with which to tackle the job. When you believe you will fail, you can't even get started.

TEN WAYS TO BUILD UP ENERGY THROUGH SELF-CONFIDENCE

So how are you going to build up this self-confidence that builds energy?

1. Act as if you already possessed self-confidence

This is the simplest and most important rule of all. It will work like a charm for you.

Just ask yourself: "What would I do today if I possessed the self-confidence I'd like to have?"

Decide what it is, and do it.

At first, you may think this is impossible. How can you act self-confidently, with all those doubts and fears holding you back?

The results of acting self-confidently. A. H. Maslow of Brandeis University tells us in *Motivation and Personality* (New York: Harper & Brothers, 1954, pp. 41–42) exactly how following this rule worked for a woman lacking in self-confidence.

She was told to act aggressively in 20 specific, apparently trivial situations. For instance, if her grocer tried to switch her from the brand she wanted as he usually did, she was to insist on her own favorite brand.

Three months after she had followed the rule of acting self-confidently every time one of the 20 situations arose, the changes in her personality were studied. She had changed so completely that even her dreams were of a different type. And her waking life was delightfully different!

Previously she had never been able to go swimming with others, because she'd been too shy to wear a bathing suit.

But with the psychologist's instructions to guide her, she had begun doing the things she'd always been too lacking in self-confidence to do before. She had bought herself a new form-fitting bathing suit and had worn it.

At one time her clothes had had all the sex appeal of potato sacks. Now she began dressing in garments that made no apology for the fact that she was a woman.

Her sexual behavior toward her husband had changed completely. Where once she had taken a purely passive attitude, so that she had seemed frigid, she now acted spontaneously in her relations with her husband. No wonder he felt as if he were married to a new and more attractive wife!

How this rule applies to you. You may say, "All right, so this woman was so timid she wouldn't wear a bathing suit in front of others. But what has that to do with me?

"My lack of self-confidence is based on nothing so trivial. Here I am, a salesman, supposed to be imbued with self-confidence, but I'm afraid to go to desirable prospects and try to sell them anything. When I get up to their doors, I feel like running away."

Do the thing and you shall have the power. Actually, this woman's case has *everything* to do with you. The principle is the same regardless of whether you're a woman who lacks the self-confidence to go to a dance, or a man who lacks the confidence to handle himself well with a big shot.

Start acting today, with the next person you meet, as if you had all the self-confidence you need. "Do the thing and you shall have the power," said Emerson.

Do the confident thing and you will eventually have the power of self-confidence.

2. Become a specialist

Become as well-informed on one subject as you can.

You needn't show off your knowledge, unless the subject is pertinent to your business, and you are asked for an opinion.

But knowing the facts and knowing them well will give you self-confidence.

The man who advances an opinion as if it were a fact may not be too favorably regarded in the business world. If he doesn't know his facts, he may be rebuffed for his empty opinions, and consequently lose faith in himself. On the other hand, the man who can marshal up enough basic information to justify his conclusions will win respect.

The importance of factual knowledge. When Bernard Baruch was acting as adviser to President Wilson, the President called him "Dr. Facts."

Alfred N. Steele, when he was chairman of the board of the Pepsi-Cola Company, told me, "My cardinal rule is never to guess at anything. Before making any important decision, we always gather the facts pertaining to it."

In order to keep your self-esteem, without which your energy will droop, be sure of your facts. The opinions of a man who is poorly informed will not be highly regarded. So before you make a positive statement, be positive you are right.

3. Put yourself in the other fellow's shoes

"What in the world," you say, "has that to do with self-confidence?"

Charles A. Cerami states this connection perfectly in *Successful Leadership in Business* (Englewood Cliffs, N. J.: Prentice-Hall, Inc., 1955, p. 37): "It is impossible to be tense or timid if you have put yourself in the other fellow's shoes before talking with him."

You may find it difficult to muster up great energy or self-confidence if your motive is to hornswoggle the other person. Only the most unethical type of person can derive energy from such a motive. But nearly all of us can get up a lot of steam if we have put ourselves in the other fellow's shoes and know that we are suggesting something that will benefit him.

A simple question to ask yourself. The simple question: "How would I feel if I were he?" will give you at least twice as much energy as you would have if you didn't ask yourself that question.

In the first place, thinking about his problems will put your mind where it should be—on him, rather than on yourself. Haven't you noticed how often those who brood about themselves tend to undermine their own self-confidence?

Secondly, if you go to any man with a recommendation for some kind of action, you'll be unconvincing and lacking in self-confidence if all you've thought about is how his decision will affect *you*. If you have done enough research on the subject *to know* that your recommendation will benefit *him*, you can be very self-confident in expressing your views.

How putting yourself in the other fellow's shoes makes you more self-confident. Let us assume that you are a salesman selling health insurance. Your prospect is interested in your recommendation, but not completely sold, until you make a simple statement that shows you have her interests at heart.

"I strongly recommend," you say, "that you add polio insurance to your policy. No one in your family may ever need it, but that simple bit of insurance, at a cost of $10 a year, will give you $5,000 worth of insurance if someone in your family should ever need it."

All of a sudden she remembers her neighbor's agony when her little girl was stricken with polio. Not only did her neighbor face the unhappiness of worrying about the child; she also had to meet mounting bills she couldn't afford. At a cost of $10 a year she could have safeguarded against such a burdensome expense.

At this moment you have convinced her that you have her interests at heart. Naturally she'll buy from you.

And what enabled you to convince her? The fact that you could self-confidently make a recommendation, knowing that it was in her best interests to follow it.

4. Know your weaknesses and strengths

If you are lacking in self-confidence, you probably know your weaknesses and dwell too seldom on your strengths. Yet strengths can be used to overcome flaws in yourself.

How one discouraged man learned where his strengths lay. One man I know was bitterly discouraged because he had failed

at many jobs.   Finally things got to the point where his wife
insisted he ought to take a series of aptitude tests, to determine
where his strengths lay.

He went to a counseling service in his city, recommended
by the American Personnel and Guidance Association.

Included among the tests he took were two on his interests,
a temperament test, and three batteries of intelligence tests.

They showed that basically he was an idealist, satisfied to
make only a moderate amount of money, provided he could do
work he would enjoy.   They also showed that although all his
life he had worked at mechanical trades, he was ideally suited
for teaching.   His IQ placed him among the highly superior
groups in this country in intelligence.

Learning that he belonged among the intellectual élite
(those with IQ's over 130) he regained some of his lost self-
confidence.   He also learned that he was only average in the
one field in which he had tried to earn a living: mechanics.
As a teacher he could satisfy his desire to help others, and use
his head instead of his hands.   He'd never before realized how
bright he really was.

Aided by the new knowledge, he took courses in teaching,
passed his teaching examinations with high grades, and obtained a position as a teacher.   He began leading a happy and
fulfilling life.

5. Visualize those whom you fear
in ridiculous situations

A young interne overcame his fears of big shots when he
discovered that he had no awe of any man, however successful,
when he had him on the operating table.   After that, whenever
he met any individual of whom he was in awe he would picture
that man in his birthday suit.   This put him at great ease.

We sometimes lose our perspective and forget that the president of a big company is only a human being after all.   You
may picture him in his home, being henpecked by a loving but
nagging wife.   Or if you prefer you may visualize him in a
nightshirt.

The absurdity of these pictures should put you in a frame

of mind where you have plenty of energy. When you're too much in awe of someone, you're apt to become nervous and lose energy, or waste your energy in nervous gestures. Instead of dwelling on your own frailties and his immense strengths, you'll profit by remembering that he may have frailties, too, and that you definitely have strengths.

6. Learn to praise yourself to yourself

Actual tests have shown that most men do better, make fewer errors, and have a great deal more energy when they are praised for what they do well.

You may have an employer who doesn't believe much in praising employees. But remember that you are also your own employer, harnessing your own energies for jobs you want to do well. So look for, notice, and praise yourself to yourself for everything you do well.

I am a great believer in the power of praise upon the unconscious mind. That includes the effects of silent self-praise.

Your friends should praise you subtly. But whether they do or not, why not be a friend to yourself?

A good friend may know your faults as well as your virtues, but he concentrates on the latter.

Paraphrasing a famous poem:
"Be to your faults a little blind,
  And to your virtues very kind."

Particularly when you are drifting off into sleep, try to remember the things you have done wisely and well that day, and give yourself a mental pat on the back. At the same time, resolve to avoid repeating your mistakes.

7. Spend time with positive-thinking individuals

Individuals who are not sure of themselves may try to build themselves up by tearing you down. When you find yourself sensitive to what others say, ask yourself: "Is his criticism justified? Does he know what he is talking about, or is he just shooting his mouth off? What are his motives? Is he trying to be constructive, or is he just tearing me down because he's in a wretched mood?"

If you find that some of your associates are 90 per cent destructive, cut down on the time you spend with them.

Spend as much time as you can with those who leave you liking yourself better after you have been with them.

8. Engage in social activities

Join at least one club. Try to play an active part there. You needn't be an officer, but if you volunteer for one committee, you will get some experience in club work that will serve you well by proving to you that you have capabilities to contribute to your group. This will add to your self-confidence, and that in turn will add to your energy.

Try to play host at your own home frequently. The first time you try it, you may feel like a nervous wreck afterwards. But with experience will come the knowledge and self-assurance that come from handling a situation over and over again.

9. Take a course in public speaking

This is probably one of the most valuable steps you can take to increase your self-confidence.

Until you have stepped up before an audience and have spoken, you may feel that you can't do it.

The fear of doing it may almost paralyze you the first time. But if you force yourself to keep going to such a class, you will eventually triumph over your nervousness.

Edward O. Morgan, who recently acted as chairman at the National Sales Executives Conference, was petrified the first time he was asked to make a speech. In fact, he wanted to refuse, but his boss told him that if he refused to address a certain audience, he would be out of a job. He delivered the speech, but did it so badly that he decided that he would have to master public speaking. He joined Toastmasters, Inc., and became a witty, delightful speaker, much sought after as an emcee.

Other men have learned through the Dale Carnegie groups, the C. C. Mullin group on the West Coast, and through courses given in high schools and adult education schools.

Your fear may be a friend. Actually, the butterflies you get in your stomach when you have to make a speech before a big audience may be good for you. The panic you feel is nature's way of coming to your rescue. Filled with fear, you then benefit from the stirring up of your adrenal glands, which pour forth hormones that give you energy.

Since you are filled with these energy-giving hormones, use them. One way is by handling papers you can give out to the audience, getting up charts to illustrate your points, keeping your hands busy by making appropriate gestures.

Intense fear always stimulates the adrenal glands. But if you let the products of those glands course through your body without *using* the energy they give you, you will be more exhausted than if you make use of this extra energy.

10. Assume the posture of a confident man

In *How to Have Confidence and Power in Dealing with People* (Englewood Cliffs, N. J.: Prentice-Hall, Inc., 1956, pp. 42–43) Les Giblin says: *"Our physical actions express our mental attitudes.* If you see a man walking along with shoulders bent and drooped, you can know that his burdens are almost too heavy for him to bear. He acts as if he were carrying a heavy weight around with him. (He probably is, in the form of discouragement and despair.) When something is weighting down a man's spirit, it invariably weights down his body. He droops . . .

"The man with a feeling of confidence steps out boldly. His shoulders are back, and his eyes are looking out and up to some goal he feels he can attain."

Since our actions influence our attitudes, you can become more self-confident by assuming the bearing of a self-confident person.

Our postures influence our thoughts. When you stand and walk erect, your whole spirit is buoyant. Your glands pour forth their happiest hormones; you feel keyed up, but not tense.

Your life and your work seem easy. You have more than

enough energy for everything. Your whole body seems to say: "Full speed ahead!"

You feel you have a date with destiny. And you do. For as Freud himself said, "Confidence of success often induces real success."

That's because it gives you so much extra energy—enough to conquer almost anything.

TEN WAYS TO BUILD UP THE SELF-CONFIDENCE THAT BUILDS UP ENERGY

1. Act as if you already possessed self-confidence.

2. Become a specialist.

3. Put yourself in the other fellow's shoes.

4. Know your weaknesses and your strengths.

5. Visualize those whom you fear in ridiculous situations.

6. Learn to praise yourself to yourself.

7. Spend as much time as you can with constructive, positive-thinking individuals.

8. Engage in social activities.

9. Take a course in public speaking, or join a group like Toastmasters, Inc., or Toastmistresses.

10. Assume the posture of a confident man.

5

How to Sleep Better for More Energy and Longer Life

ONCE UPON A TIME THERE WAS A COLLEGE STUDENT WHO BE-
lieved that sleep is nothing but a bad habit which might be
overcome, like other habits, by a determined effort. He went
to his physiology professor, an authority on sleep problems,
and stated his theory.

"Would you be willing to test it under my supervision?"
asked the professor. "I'd like to try an experiment on the
effects of sleeplessness."

The student cheerfully agreed.

To keep track of his wakefulness, he was given a night watch-
man's clock that registered the time every ten minutes.

For the first few days, everything went well. His pulse
rate, weight, and blood pressure remained normal.

Your mind can be affected by prolonged sleeplessness. On
the fourth day he began to see things that weren't there, and
to hear voices no one else could hear. His physical stamina
still seemed fine. His blood pressure and pulse rate were still
normal.

But day after day he became more irrational. He found it
difficult to think straight, to remember things he had done
only five or ten minutes previously. He even had symptoms
of a persecution complex.

Altogether he stayed awake 231 hours, with only 5¼ hours of sleep in ten to 30 minute snatches.

You can, however, easily make up for severe sleep deprivation.   When I asked Dr. Nathaniel Kleitman, who has studied sleep phenomena for over 35 years, how long it took this student to recover, he said, "I do not know how long it took him to get over the effects, but my guess would be: one night's sleep."

Nevertheless, regular sleep does help toward better health and much more abundant energy.

You'll live longer if you sleep regularly and well.   The value of regular sleep in giving us greater energy and a longer life span has even been accepted by insurance actuaries.

One day a group of them discussed the methods available for judging the future longevity of those seeking insurance. They found that one trait marked all of the long-lived individuals they had studied statistically.   Asked how many hours of sleep they averaged nightly, they answered cheerfully, "Seven or eight hours every night, not just as an average, but *regularly*."

Almost invariably, individuals who could truthfully report this lived longer than the norm.

So if you want more energy and longer life, let us see what you should know about the latest discoveries on how to sleep better.

TEN WAYS TO BAIT SLEEP

1. Don't get too keyed up during the day

One day, preceding an interview with a television personality for a magazine article, I had lunch with a public relations executive who handled this account for a large advertising agency.

The public relations man was obviously upset, and ordered a double strength martini before lunch.

Noticing his agitation, I asked him about it.

A stressful situation.   "It happens every week at about this time," he told me. "This is the day on which we hold our conference with the sponsors of the TV program. One of their representatives is a very critical man. I know that I am expected to make suggestions. No matter what suggestion I make, he will object to it, criticize it, and make me feel small."

A situation like this one that involves conflict is the kind of stressful activity during the day that causes extreme nervous tension, a resultant inability to relax, and finally inability to sleep well at night.

The two alternatives in a stressful situation. You might very well say, "Well, what could he do about it? Meeting such a stressful situation is part of his job, isn't it?"

It is. Under such circumstances, it is sometimes necessary to choose between a too stressful job and less money at a less tense job. In many cases, resigning from the job requires too substantial a financial sacrifice.

If you decide to stick with the job in spite of the strain, there are several things you can do to lessen the tension.

The night before the conference, you must do your best to relax every muscle. Authorities on relaxation tell us that when our *bodies* are completely relaxed, we cannot worry.

Before you go to sleep, give yourself this positive mental suggestion: "I shall wake up in the morning feeling cool, calm, and collected. Later in the day I shall not let anything disturb me."

Before the conference, flash these words to your inner mind, "Cool, calm, and collected right now and all through the conference."

If you have to face a difficult individual, remember that he is probably not as sure of himself as he pretends to be. His inner insecurity is what drives him to badger you.

Recipe for mental poise in stressful situations. Ray Baird, the consulting engineer who today has tremendous mental poise, told me, "At one time I had to do business with a railroading type of individual. He always gave the impression of being self-confident, and of being contemptuous of almost everybody else.

"I never had words with him about it, but over the years did my best to develop my own mental poise.

"A few weeks ago, when I met him again, I noticed an unusual change. Instead of giving the impression of being self-confident, he gave just the opposite impression.

"I got to thinking about mental poise. It is like a competitive battle. We are trying to develop a mental poise greater than that possessed by others around us.

"Poise is that characteristic that keeps us from losing control when something unusual occurs. It is the ability to ride through adverse situations without becoming nervous and jittery. The way to develop it is to go out of your way to meet, talk with, and associate with all kinds of people in social and professional situations."

It is not always possible to avoid all stressful situations during the day. But it is possible to avoid getting too keyed up about those situations.

Relax after a tense situation. Spend evening hours quietly. If you must face stressful activities during the day, try to get over your tenseness during the late afternoon and evening hours.

If you have important plans to make for the next day, make them a couple of hours before you go to sleep, rather than in the precious hour before bedtime when you should be operating on the lowest possible key of tenseness.

Use the last hour of the day for quiet relaxation with a not too exciting book, or watching an amusing TV show, or talking quietly to a congenial companion, preferably someone who is not too tense and nervous.

2. Plan for variety

This is particularly important if your job is somewhat monotonous.

Fatigue is much easier to prevent than to cure. If you will divide monotonous jobs into one-hour or two-hour periods and stop *before* you are tired, you will not be as exhausted as when you continue without stopping. Work for eight or ten hours without stopping or changing the type of work you are doing, and you will be so exhausted you won't be able to fall asleep readily.

For instance, suppose you are working in an office where your job consists of writing letters to important customers, keeping accounts, and filing. In that case, you'd be wise to do your most creative work—writing the letters—first. The filing would probably be the most monotonous job, so you'd be better off dividing your filing into two periods of an hour each, rather than spending two continuous hours at the task.

A friend of mine, Roberta Lee Gill, head of the duplicating department of Fluor's in Los Angeles, has trained all the girls who work for her so that each of them can take care of any operation in the department.

She knows that a girl working at a long form in the multilith machine will grow tired of looking at the darned thing. So after a couple of hours' run at this machine, she will shift her to something else: stripping negatives, handling a short run, or bulletins, or working with colored paper. Meantime, another girl completes the monotonous job.

Another type of work that is apt to be tiresome is handling a varityper, so after a girl has used one for a couple of hours, she will relieve her of the task and turn over this job to someone else.

If you are a supervisor, controlling the time of others, you can get better work out of them by never asking anyone to work at a monotonous job more than two hours at a time. Even if you switch a worker from one monotonous job to another, it is not as tiring as working four hours at the same job.

If you control your own time, vary your jobs. If you don't, boredom will bring on the kind of fatigue that makes relaxed sleep difficult.

Most of the writers I know, including myself, vary writing with research, interviewing, reading newspapers and magazines, and filing. Professional article writers like myself must read a number of magazines and newspapers each day.

Clipping these can be tiresome, and most writers would get

very annoyed if they had to spend eight hours a day at this. But by spending an hour or two a day at this task, a writer can keep up with what's going on.

3. Try to stick to as regular hours as possible

Dr. Nathaniel Kleitman of the Department of Physiology of the University of Chicago considers this one of the greatest promoters of sound, regular, healthful sleep.

He tells us: "This does not mean that the individual must never deviate from a routine of existence. The resulting dullness of life would probably be a higher price than most of us might be willing to pay." (Kleitman, Nathaniel. *Sleep and Wakefulness.* Reprinted by permission of the University of Chicago Press. Copyright 1939 by the University of Chicago.)

What amount of regularity will bring peaceful sleep to you and me? That is something each of us must decide individually. However, I have found that in my circle of acquaintances, most of the men who work hard five days a week usually stay up late at least two nights a week. By filling those nights with joyful recreation, they give some color to their lives. Perhaps one night might be spent bowling; another evening might be spent at a dinner party with congenial friends.

4. Avoid situations that leave you with tensions, regret

You can't afford the kind of excitement that leaves you with an abnormal sense of guilt. You also can't afford the kind of sex excitement that offers no fulfillment in a normal sex act. (For more about the relation between sex and energy, see Chapter 9.)

I can still remember a bit of verse that was popular during my adolescence:

> A little petting now and then
> Is relished by the best of men.

Undoubtedly this is true. Yet it puts a man in quite a dilemma, for petting arouses our most primitive instincts. If the girl involved has indicated that she'll go this far and no further, the man will undoubtedly feel a sense of physical frustration.

Parking in dark spots in your Chrysler Imperial and going as far as you dare with the girl of your choice may seem exciting; but the frustration of having her say "no" before the final step will drain your energy and give you a sleepless night. Consequently sex excitement should be avoided as much as possible, unless you know ahead of time that the final culmination will be a release, not a building up of your tensions.

The wild drinking party is also apt to result in sleepless nights. A glass of burgundy before bedtime may be a fine nightcap; but if you take four or five drinks to relax just before bedtime, you may find yourself over-stimulated instead of relaxed. Many individuals, it is true, find it easy to drop off to sleep when they've had too many drinks. However, they often wake up a few hours later tense and unrelaxed, because too much liquor does have bad after-effects.

By all means, avoid the kind of party where you're apt to finish the night off with somebody else's wife.

This isn't simply a matter of morality, or even of good taste. Sooner or later you will probably pay in sleepless nights for this kind of "self-expression." Most of us have an inner conscience to reckon with, which doesn't approve of such goings on, no matter how sophisticated the crowd with which we run. And when our inner conscience is disturbed, our sleep is disturbed.

If you're going to a dance, choose one sponsored by a wholesome group, like the Masons, the Elks, or your church affiliation. If you're going to a party, pay some attention to who your host is. If you insist on running with a wildly bohemian crowd, you will eventually pay in disillusionment, loss of sleep, and an empty pocketbook.

5. Adopt a sleep ritual

Start a ritual that *you* associate with sleeping soundly. Actually, the nature of the ritual is not nearly as important as the fact that you use it regularly every night, and believe that it will help you. It may be walking the dog around the block, a warm or tepid bath (my personal favorite), a drink of hot milk, or brushing your hair twenty times.

Any one of these actions, repeated regularly each night, can become your private, personal sleep conditioner.

6. Keep a sleep diary

Are you at your best after eight hours, seven hours, or six hours of sleep?

There is actually nothing sacred about eight hours of sleep. The figure is used because it's convenient to divide the day into three sections. Naturally, if you're accustomed to eight hours' sleep, you may feel drowsy after an evening in which you spend only six hours in bed.

Dr. Kleitman has found that seven and a half hours is the average among the subjects he has tested. One man may find six hours plenty, and another may feel that nine hours are hardly enough.

You should test yourself for about a month to find out what your best sleep pattern is.

If you are accustomed to eight hours of sleep, you might try for one week getting along on seven and a half hours a night. If you find that this reduces your energy markedly, you can then go back to your usual eight hours.

There are other facts about your sleep habits you should study and record. Do you sleep better after a warm bath? If you drink coffee after 6 P.M., does it interfere with your night's rest?

For the next month, keep a diary in which you record the conditions preceding sleep. Include the time you took your last cup of coffee. Some individuals suffer badly from too much caffeine in the late hours of the evening, says Dr. Kleitman. Others are affected by the *belief* that caffeine affects them.

At one time Dr. Kleitman was experimenting with the effects of caffeine on his students. One group was given capsules containing milk sugar, another capsules containing some caffeine.

The students were not told what their groups were receiving. On one occasion a student was under the impression that he had received a large, perhaps poisonous dose of caffeine. Frightened, he went across a small court to the hospital, where he reported palpitation of the heart and other symptoms.

"His stomach was pumped out," Dr. Kleitman told me, "but he was quite embarrassed to learn next day that all he got that night was milk sugar."

"Some persons," adds Dr. Kleitman, "have difficulty in falling asleep after they have had some coffee in the evening."

Your sleep diary will show what the real effect of caffeine is on *you*.

What about your nighttime snack? Try going to bed tonight after a light repast of hot milk or some fruit. Try going to bed tomorrow night without any food at all after your regular dinner.

Your results should show what is right for *you*.

In one series of experiments, a group of individuals slept better after drinking a patented substance mixed with hot milk. However, when the same group tried hot milk without the patented substance, they slept just as soundly.

Don't overdo the midnight snack. A hearty steak is a poor choice for an 11 P.M. supper if you're going to bed at midnight.

7. Learn to relax your mind as well as your body

Sleep that completely restores your energy depends on physical and mental relaxation.

Try progressive relaxation. Edmund Jacobson, M.D., has successfully taught progressive physical relaxation to his patients. He believes that one should learn to relax one's arms, one's legs, one's chest, tongue, and throat muscles, etc.—one step at a time—then combine relaxation of all the muscles for better sleep.

In *learning* to relax, it is sometimes advisable to tense a particular part of the body first, then let go, let go, let go, to get the sense of what the difference is between tension and relaxation. Once you have recognized the sensation of tenseness, do not continue to practice tenseness; practice rest and relaxation, without effort. Effort is the opposite of relaxation.

Relax not only your muscles; relax your thoughts. Your thoughts as you prepare for sleep can cause you to sleep well or badly. No bed is large enough to hold you comfortably, with your regrets about yesterday, and your anxieties about tomorrow.

Jim is a man who hasn't been able to sleep well in years because he always takes the past, the present, and the future to bed with him.

The effects of taking yesterday and tomorrow to bed with you. Years ago, his brother-in-law offered him an opportunity to get in on the ground floor in a certain enterprise, a discount house. Believing it was too much of a gamble, Jim turned it down.

However, to his surprise, it turned out very well. Today his brother-in-law is prosperous, but a stranger grabbed the chance he turned down. Now it's too late for him to get into the business, as the stranger is a full partner and wouldn't be willing to accept him in the firm.

When Jim goes to bed at night, he always takes this thought with him: "If only I'd accepted his offer!"

That thought is destroying him. He cannot accept the fact that the past is past, and once we have learned what we can from it, it is best not to torture ourselves with what *might* have been.

That "if only" thought is destroying not only all possibility of sleep, but also depriving him of the energy he needs to make successful decisions during the day.

When he has an important decision to make, it is likely to be a foolish one, because most of his energy is devoted, not to handling each problem as it comes up, but to regretting the problem he failed to handle correctly in the past.

When he isn't fretting over the past, he worries over what

tomorrow will bring. Carrying his fear of tomorrow with him to bed, he spends sleepless nights.

If you are the kind of person who takes yesterday and tomorrow to bed with you, you must learn to substitute other thoughts. In addition to a physical routine that will condition you for sleep, like the warm bath before retiring, you may need a mental conditioner.

Use autosuggestion. Why not whisper a phrase or thought to yourself that relaxes you completely? This is really autosuggestion.

Don't let the word frighten you. We are all using autosuggestion all the time, and our autosuggestions can be either harmful or helpful. "I'm so worried," "I can't sleep," "I can't stand it," etc., are harmful, foolish suggestions to feed to one's inner mind.

"I'm not worried" won't work either, because one's conscious mind immediately says, "You liar!" The conscious mind will not let any thought through that it considers a lie. You must choose an autosuggestion that the conscious mind will *not* challenge.

After relaxing your shoulders, neck, feet, and hands, you might use this autosuggestion suggested by Dr. Hornell Hart, Ph.D., of the Department of Sociology of Duke University (*Autoconditioning:* Englewood Cliffs, N. J.: Prentice-Hall, Inc., 1956): "You are becoming deeply peaceful. You are going to rest. You are letting go completely."

The best mental conditioners do not challenge your mind to think too deeply, too seriously.

In fact, I like this suggestion from Dr. Hornell Hart:

"Think your blood away from your brain." He feels that it will be easier to go to sleep if you think of the blood in your body as flowing away from the brain into hands and feet. Instead of putting the idea into specific words, try to imagine the feeling of the flow from the head down toward your body, toward the hands and feet.

Dr. Hart says: "The particular words employed are not the

important consideration. What matters is that when you are
ready for sleep you fill your mind as completely as possible with
the idea and the thought of deeper and deeper relaxation, and
a more and more complete letting go of tensions, more and
more submission to fatigue, drowsiness, slumber, and sleep."

Personally, I think the less you employ words to put you to
sleep, the better.

A *feeling* of being at peace with the world is far more helpful than the actual words: "I am at peace with the world."
Use the words only if you cannot achieve the feeling *without*
the words.

Say your prayers before going to bed at night. To some
this may seem naïve. There are individuals who believe that
prayer has no effect upon one's bodily activities. But science
has proved again and again that one's attitude toward God, as
expressed in prayer, may determine whether one can sleep
easily or not.

One writer advised that those who want to sleep well should
get in front of an open window, and take two deep breaths.
Then he added that prayer would do just as well.

No reason why you can't take the two deep breaths and
pray, too!

*A poet's secret for falling asleep the moment his head
touched a pillow.* Edwin Markham, the poet, was asked by a
friend how he was able to fall asleep as soon as his head
touched a pillow.

"I figure that the same God who has taken care of everything throughout the world through all the centuries will be
able to run the universe without my assistance for seven or
eight hours each night," he explained.

*A feeling of happy and complete forgiveness of oneself and
everyone else is necessary before one can sleep peacefully.*
One reason prayer and faith help so much is because they give
us the incentive to forgive those we feel have trespassed against
us, and the assurance that God is forgiving us.

If you have done something you feel really ashamed of, try
to repair any harm you have done before you go to bed at

night.   If you can't, resolve just before you go to bed that you will make those amends as soon as possible, preferably the next morning.

If you have said something unkind or untrue, don't hesitate to apologize.   One of my friends says: "Lots of men and women hate to eat humble pie, but when you are really ashamed of the way you've acted, humble pie can taste mighty good!"

If, just as you are about to drop into a tired sleep, an angry or hostile thought comes to your mind, say quietly to yourself about the person who has hurt you, "God bless him."

One man told me that whenever he saw someone hideous or deformed or saw someone behaving badly, he said to himself, "God bless him," and his feeling of tension and loathing passed.

Free your mind of all problems.   It may be all right for you to think briefly about a problem before you try to sleep; then turn it over to the unconscious mind to solve.   You may say to your unconscious, "Please let me know tomorrow morning what I can do or say to persuade the boss to give me a raise." Have complete faith in the ability of your unconscious to solve the problem.   Shut off your conscious thoughts by shutting off your throat muscles.

Silence your throat muscles to fall asleep.   As a writer, I had formed the habit of reciting silently to myself certain ideas that I hoped to put into articles the next day.   So even when the day's work was done, my sub-vocal throat muscles were apt to keep on jiggling.   To fall asleep, I found I had to quiet those throat muscles completely.   Once they become relaxed, I find it easy to doze off.

Some individuals talk to themselves for hours in bed; tell themselves their troubles and problems before they fall asleep.

Was Morpheus ever successfully wooed in this manner? Never!

When you begin to go over and over the same mental ground like a broken record, stop it quickly.   Relax those throat muscles.   Stop talking to your mind.   As long as it is listening, you'll stay awake.

8. Don't worry about your supposed inability to sleep

First of all, you may be getting a lot more sleep than you think. Complete sleeplessness for several nights is rare indeed.

Secondly, relaxation in bed is almost as helpful as sleep. It's been estimated that lying in bed quietly is about 75 per cent as useful to the repair processes of the body as complete sleep.

One professor of philosophy who died at the age of 91 confessed to his students that he used to sleep only an hour or two each night. But he always remained quietly in bed resting so that the next morning he felt fresh.

It is helpful to remember that as we grow older, we usually need less sleep. Older folk should not think they are being cheated if they can't sleep as many hours as when they were younger. If you are waking up too early, you might try going to bed an hour later each night. Even if that means that you go to bed after midnight, don't worry about it. Careful experimentation has established the fact that contrary to popular opinion, an hour of sleep *after* midnight *is* just as effective as an hour *before* midnight.

To test just how much sleep you do need, try a week of going to bed every night at the same hour, and see at just what time you naturally wake up.

Sleep is the great restorer of your energy. Second best is bed rest without actual slumber.

Many authorities on healthful sleep regard your physical well-being and energy as a kind of bank from which you must make many withdrawals each day. Naturally, the bank would rapidly become depleted if you didn't make some deposits.

Regular hours of rest are probably the most valuable of all the deposits you can make to your energy bank.

IN A NUTSHELL:
EIGHT WAYS TO SLEEP BETTER

1. Don't get too keyed up during the day.

2. Don't spend long periods of time on one activity, but plan your day for variety.

3. *Try to stick to the same waking and sleeping hours as much as possible, within reason.*

4. *Avoid situations that leave you filled with regret and tensions.*

5. *Adopt a sleep ritual, doing the same thing every night before bedtime.*

6. *Keep a sleep diary, to find out what's best for you.*

7. *Learn to relax your mind as well as your body. To help you relax your mind, say your prayers before going to bed at night.*

8. *Never get into a stew about your supposed inability to sleep, but learn to rest quietly when unable to sleep.*

Part 2

HOW TO STOP
SQUANDERING ENERGY

6

How to Control Energy-
Squandering Anger

WE COME INTO THIS WORLD EQUIPPED WITH A MAGNIFICENT capital of energy. No one could truthfully put an honest monetary value on it. However, this energy is worth to you exactly what life itself is worth. Personally, I value at an astronomical figure the vitality with which I was born.

Your amazing capital of energy. Let us say that you come endowed with ten billion dollars' worth of energy. You are capable of magnificent things. Like Wordsworth's infant, you come not only "trailing clouds of glory," but with a potential energy no one can estimate.

A wise and generous Father has arranged matters so that you can usually draw only limited amounts of this vitality at a time. But you not only have a nice cash fund of energy from day to day to draw upon; you have a remarkable reserve account, too.

Yet in spite of this great fund, you may grow into a weary, listless, unhappy man, conscious of continual fatigue. Where did your great energy go?

We'd be labeled insane if we threw money away so recklessly. No man could stay out of an asylum if he threw his money around as recklessly as some of us fling our energy away.

If a man were to stand on a street corner and toss pieces of long green to every passerby, he'd soon be locked up for observation. Yet this is precisely the way many of us treat our God-given energies.

It is not enough to be born with a vast amount of energy; we have to use it selectively. Why toss it away on passing whims, on foolish emotions, on every childish impulse that comes to us?

Perhaps one of the greatest destroyers of energy is an emotion some men are foolishly proud of. Many hot-tempered individuals kid themselves that their bad tempers are evidence of their masculinity. Actually, nothing of the sort is true. An easily aroused temper is usually a sign that you have not yet laid away childish thoughts.

Anger can waste our energy in two ways. If we grow furious at someone and repress our anger, it may fester inside us like poison. Chronic anger becomes hostility, and an attitude of hostility toward others will make us chronically tired.

For instance, there was Joe, a young man who suffered from a seemingly perpetual fatigue. He was so chronically tired that he had to give up his job. Actually, if he hadn't resigned, his boss would have been compelled to fire him, because he was accomplishing about two hours' honest work in an eight hour day.

His wife finally insisted on Joe's seeing a psychiatrist. The psychiatrist discovered that when Joe was a youngster, he was bitterly jealous of his younger brother. One day the two boys had an argument; he slapped and scratched the brother's face, and told him, "I wish you were dead."

When his mother learned what had happened, she was shocked. She locked Joe into the bathroom, and wouldn't let him come out until he apologized to his brother, and uttered the lying words, "I love you. I didn't mean what I said."

From that time on, he tried to repress the murderous rage within him, in order to win his mother's approval. But his mother always seemed to favor his brother. He grew up full of hostility toward his brother. Since he was doing his best to repress his anger, his murderous thoughts found shape only in his dreams, in which night after night, he dreamed that his brother had died.

Because of his hostile, repressed wishes, he had a great sense of guilt. The battle he fought within himself against this inner guilt wearied him so much he had no strength left with which to fight the external battles that came up in his work. The more he repressed his inner hostility, the more tired he became.

So we can grow fatigued because of repressed hatred and anger.

The second way in which anger can use up our energy is when we unloose it.

Anger is paradoxical in its effects on energy. It is one of the most deceptive emotions, so far as its effect on energy is concerned. It builds up your energy temporarily, only to let you down completely at the end.

There is no denying the fact that a rush of anger brings a a rush of energy-building substances to the muscles. In fact, science now says that the adrenalin released by anger causes the liver to convert its glycogen into blood sugar, which is then rushed to the muscles. Momentarily, your strength may be as the strength of ten, because you are angry. And yet the final effect is often complete exhaustion!

The immediate effect of anger. If it were possible to harness anger as primitive men did, we might all be supermen. The immediate effect of anger is a tremendous supply of *physical* energy.

An interesting example of the amazing physical strength with which anger endows us is related by Elise Miller Davis in an article entitled, "A Man Don't Know What He Can Do" (Reader's Digest, October 1952).

A truck driver, Roy Gaby, who was driving for a Houston, Texas, trucking company, was caught helplessly in a truck cab. In swerving to avoid a collision with a speeding car driven by a drunken passenger, he had crashed into an oak tree; the trailer had piled up on the cab, and Roy had been trapped in the middle of the debris.   The truck began burning, and there were tiny flames at his feet, which were caught and pinned under by broken parts of the cab.   He lay encased in the wrecked vehicle like a sardine in a can.

Three trucks and a wrecker had tried to budge that truck cab without success.   Then a husky Negro suddenly appeared, and said to the Deputy Sheriff, "Is it all right if I help?"   He walked over to the cab.   Then continues Elise Miller Davis, "He put his hands on the door and *wrenched it off!*"

He put out the flames with his bare hands; then poking his large arms into the truck cab, he straightened the steering wheel and pulled Gaby's feet free.

Fury gave this man abnormal physical strength.   "It was just about then that I caught a glimpse of the big fellow's face," one witness said, according to Miss Davis.   "At first I thought he was in a trance.   Then I saw that set expression for what it was—cold, calculated *fury*.   I'd seen an expression like that before on a man's face.   It was at Pearl Harbor.   I'd seen it again on men's faces at Okinawa.   I remember thinking, 'That man's enraged!' "

The witness was right.   Spurred on by rage, the Negro pushed his way into the burning truck, pushed up the top, and held it up until the Deputy Sheriff and his men were able to pull the truck driver out.

Deputy Sheriff Don Henry told reporters later, "If I hadn't witnessed it, I'd never have believed that one lone man could do a job we couldn't do with three trucks and a wrecker."

The secret of super-strength in emergencies.   What was the secret of the unknown Samson's strength?   Newspapermen learned it later.   The young Negro was Charles Dennis Jones. On a December night 14 months previously his eight-year-old daughter, Evelyn Carol, had been burned to death by a flash fire that had destroyed his home.   He had saved her from the fire, only to have her run back again into the flaming house because she wanted to rescue her Christmas lights.   He had raced after her, but before he could reach her, the whole building had exploded.   And a little wraith in a white gown had died in that burning building.

From that time on, Charles Dennis Jones had hated flames with an almost physical hatred.   When he saw another human being menaced by flames that crept around his feet, anger enveloped him against the destroying monster that had robbed him of his first-born child.

The rage he felt at the sight of a human being whose life was being menaced by fire caused a definite chemical change in his body that gave him super-energy and super-power.

Anger is a preparation for action.   The extraordinary physical strength given us by anger illustrates why primitive man was endowed with the ability to get angry.   Anger, our physiologists tell us, prepares the body for two possible reactions: fight or flight.

Anger sometimes prepares us for the wrong actions.   The trouble with most angry reactions is that they equip you for a primitive type of world: a world of savagery, murder, and of constant danger, where physical strength means everything.

Today, the physical reactions for which anger equips you— fight and flight—are rarely necessary or desirable.   Compromise is often a better way of dealing with most situations than wrath.   Anger is a spendthrift emotion, which squanders energy.

That's why the Bible tell us in Proverbs XVI: "He that is slow to anger is better than the mighty; and he that ruleth his spirit than he that taketh a city."

Anger prepares the body for violent action.   We may be tempted to attack the person who angers us, but we know darned well that if we do, we'll get into trouble with the police.   So we usually refrain from carrying out that first violent impulse.

However, all the forces of the body have now been marshaled for action.   "Action!   Action!   Action!" screams the body.   Our blood pressure rises; our hearts beat faster; our blood flows toward the muscles; our fists clench.

We resist our murderous impulses.   We know that we must.

Why anger eventually exhausts us.   Our anger has freed large quantities of adrenalin and norepinephrine, which are extremely stimulating chemicals.

And what do these chemicals do?   According to a team of research medical scientists at Lankenau Hospital, Philadelphia, within half an hour they force the heart to work more than four times as hard as three cocktails would.   The three cocktails, the researchers said, increase the heart's work 20 per cent.   Adrenalin, released by anger, increases its work 90 per cent.

Now, if the emergency were of such a nature as to call for physical exertion, this would be very helpful.   But most of us who become violently angry are like a group of fire fighters who have answered a false alarm.   Normally we cannot beat into submission the enemies who have angered us.

Consequently, the only thing to do is to go back to the firehouse and report the real state of affairs.   By this time, we have devoted so much energy in getting ready for an intense and dangerous battle that we are completely fatigued.

If we can't use our energies in action, they exhaust us.   At the end of a period of anger that we can't fully express, we are much wearier than if we hadn't become angry.

Chronic anger can make us ill.   So serious is the effect of internal fury on our health that one psychiatrist suggested that one of his clients throw darts at the photograph of the president of his company, at whom he was very angry.   The psychiatrist knew that a direct expression of his client's anger might lose him his job, and that in addition it would exhaust him physically and spiritually.   On the other hand, he was afraid that if the man *suppressed* his anger, it might make him ill.

The habit of *letting yourself get angry*, particularly over many small provocations, can also make you ill.

Says Frank S. Caprio, M.D., the noted psychiatrist, in *Helping Yourself with Psychiatry*: (Englewood Cliffs, N.J.: Prentice-Hall, Inc., 1957, p. 188): "The man who always flies into a rage when anything upsets him is apt to succumb to a cerebral accident. A person suffering from high blood pressure surely doesn't benefit from spells of anger. Hate is an ulcer-producing emotion, can cause headaches and nervous skin rashes, can take away your appetite, keep you awake at night, cause your marriage to fail, jeopardize your job, and alienate you from your fellow man. Hate makes you *tense*. Love makes you *relax*."

Hate and rage are intimately tied up with each other. If you hate someone, you will grow angry at him very readily. If you grow angry at someone easily, you will resent the emotional exhaustion that follows—and hate the person you blame. If you grow angry at yourself, you will even hate yourself.

Living as we do in an imperfect world, it is probably impossible for anyone but a saint *never* to become angry.

One study at Swarthmore College, Pennsylvania, showed that a group of male undergraduates grew angry on an average of about twice a week for each student. A study of women at the same college indicated that most of the women grew angry about three times a week.

Very few of the reasons for their anger made very much sense. In many cases, their rage was caused by such trivial incidents as the fact that when one student came down late to the breakfast table, he found that all the biscuits were gone. Another student was angry because he found a foolish remark scribbled in a library book, and didn't have an eraser with him with which to erase it.

Occasionally, there were serious provocations for anger, like an argument with a fellow student in which the other exhibited marked prejudice toward a minority group.

Most of the students expressed their anger through various degrees of violence, usually by explosive words or gestures. In almost every case, these violent reactions were followed by periods of remorse and shame, and by fatigue.

Their fits of anger produced a vicious cycle. When they were over-tired, they grew angry more easily; and when they grew angry, they tired very easily. The after-effects of anger proved unpleasant, exhausting energy in almost every instance.

Anger is apt to make us temporarily stupid. Besides its unhappy final effects on our energy and health, anger is a dangerous emotion to succumb to, for another reason. It unleashes physical energy by drawing away blood from our brains to our muscles, so that if we act on our anger, our action is apt to be just plain stupid.

The way in which angry impulses can make you say and do the wrong thing is well illustrated by a story told by my friend, David Epstein, a very successful public relations counselor, who has handled public relations for such noted Hollywood figures as Leo McCarey, Henry King, Jerry Wald, George Sidney, and many others.

You will regret your angry words. "One day," David told me, "I was driving into Palm Springs when I saw a sign that made me sit up and take notice. The sign read: 'Never hesitate to speak your mind when you are angry. It will be the finest speech you will ever regret having made.'

"I had a personal experience once that taught me the lesson stated by that sign. I handled public relations for a client who said that he would be eternally grateful for the job I had done for him. I had been successful in handling a very delicate, ticklish public relations problem.

"When I sent him his bill, he phoned me, and his voice was troubled. When he began questioning my charges, I mistook his bewilderment for belligerency. The fact that he questioned them, after I had done such a difficult job for him, infuriated me. The charges I had made were all normal, ordinary ones, such as any public relations counselor would have made.

"In no uncertain terms I told him what I thought of him. " 'Why, you cheap, chiseling no good,' I said, 'if you're that anxious to save your money, you needn't send me a cent. I don't ever again want to have anything to do with you.'

"The moment he hung up, I knew that I had made a stupid mistake. I should have realized that he had had no previous experience with public relations counselors, and therefore hadn't realized that certain expenses have to be charged to the client.

"I should have explained those charges to him in detail, instead of accusing him of trying to chisel. The next morning, I felt worse than ever, when I received his check in the mail for the full amount of the bill."

Anger can destroy a previously pleasant relationship. "We have never spoken to each other since," David Epstein told me. "In five minutes of anger, I had destroyed a pleasant relationship that might have continued throughout both our lifetimes if I hadn't lost my temper."

Anger first builds up, then wastes energy. After his angry outburst, David Epstein felt not only regret, but also exhaustion. The temporary flurry of energy that led him to make the greatest speech he has ever regretted deserted him, and he was useless to his clients the rest of that day. Anger, it is true, gives us great temporary energy, but in the end it takes away more than it gives.

In one study of the effects of anger, two-thirds of the subjects admitted that their irritated feelings left them badly exhausted.

In one report to the American Psychiatric Association, Dr. Irving D. Harris said that many individuals suffer from ill health because of chronic resentment that they have tried to bottle up.

Whether you repress your feelings of hostility or express them in angry words and acts, you will be robbing yourself of energy and health. Bottled up anger affects the entire involuntary nervous system.

When the unconscious mind receives the command, "Hate! Hate! Hate!" your vital organs may easily be affected. Your muscles become tense.

This continued muscular tension causes a great decrease in creatine phosphate, which we need for high energy. When you hate, it's a form of stress. You are involved in an internal battle in which you yourself are the victim.

Your unconscious mind may even receive the command:

"Punish yourself for the hate you feel. You have no right to feel that way."

The self-punishment may take the form of migraine headaches, ulcers, or severe indigestion. Every part of your body that ordinarily functions automatically and perfectly can go out of kilter through your own reactions of hatred and anger.

Dr. Frank S. Caprio tells us in *Helping Yourself With Psychiatry* of Thelma, whose father was a bully and whose sister had always been abusive, when she was a child.

Thelma hated them, but tried to bottle up her feelings, because she believed it wrong to hate one's relatives. However, after her marriage, she became too ill and too tired, so she said, to take care of her children.

Actually, her chronic tiredness was the result of emotional fatigue, caused by her chronic anger against her father and sister. Unconsciously, she wanted to be too ill to take care of her children, so that the responsibility would fall on them. In response to her unconscious wish, she was ill and chronically fatigued. Her husband couldn't afford to pay the tremendous bills she incurred through her illness, so her father paid them. Her sister took care of her two children.

This made her feel guilty. She felt that she should be grateful to her father and sister, but her hostility was too great to permit her to feel any real gratitude to them.

"Doctor Caprio, I love my father and sister," she said. But further study brought out the fact of her inner hostility. She was cured of her nervous fatigue only when she learned the true nature of her feelings.

On the other hand, blowing your top at frequent intervals is not only hard on those around you, but also hard on your heart. A choleric man may be flirting with heart trouble and high blood pressure. Let's try to avoid that kind of flirtation.

Since bottling up anger and blowing your top frequently are both unsatisfactory ways of dealing with explosive situations, we must find some other methods. There are two satisfactory methods: (1) trying to avoid getting angry and (2) working off anger in harmless physical activities, when you've been unable to avoid getting angry. Let's take each of these two methods in turn.

FIVE WAYS TO KEEP FROM GETTING ANGRY

1. When you see someone else getting angry in conversation with you, notice how he expresses his fury.

Does he clench his fists? Does his face turn red? Do his eyes bulge? Perhaps you can become so absorbed in watching him make a donkey of himself that you can avoid doing likewise.

2. Think of the person who normally makes you angry as a fictional character.

How would you describe him? What explanation would you give for his characteristics? Why is he the kind of person he is?

Normally, we become angry because our own feelings are involved in a situation. We find it hard to be objective, because a slighting remark has been made about us or someone dear to us.

If, instead of concentrating on our own hurt feelings, we try to take an impersonal attitude, we may be able to avoid getting angry. Thinking about the person who is being nasty as a fictional character may enable you to preserve the kind of impersonal attitude you'd have if someone else described a situation that made *him* angry.

Even if you saw the justification for his anger, it is unlikely that you would get angry, because your own emotions wouldn't be involved. By regarding angry persons as "characters," you can achieve a more impersonal attitude.

3. Talk as little as possible to an angry person, and keep your voice down.

When you become angry, you talk more loudly. When you talk more loudly, you are apt to become more angry.

If you will remember deliberately to lower your voice whenever you are tempted to become angry, it will help you to control your own angry feelings, and also those of your adversary.

4. Try to avoid the kind of situations and discussions that are apt to lead to hot arguments.

The occasions when we should tell the other fellow off are few and far between.   Only when keeping quiet will make you contemptuous of yourself afterwards are you justified in getting into a hot argument.   A young man I know was unable to work for weeks after a provoking incident, because his own behavior left him ill with self-contempt.   When a snob of his acquaintance had criticized his father's foreign accent, he had not objected.   The fact that he had allowed an acquaintance to get away with such contemptible criticism preyed on his mind; it made him feel guilty.

However, under normal circumstances, situations worthy of a real battle rarely arise.   More frequently, we're apt to become angry because our vanity is pricked, or because we have allowed ourselves the undesirable luxury of being irritable.

Some individuals deliberately bring on anger-provoking situations.   Perhaps they like the excitement.   Or possibly, filled with hostility, they try to create a situation in which they can feel justified in expressing that hostility.

One day a group of Americans, including my husband and myself, went on a trip by auto to Tijuana in Mexico.   One of the members of the party was a girl I'll call Anna.   Unknown to the rest of us, she had been harboring resentment against her husband, perhaps because she considered him her inferior intellectually.   Many times she had tried to provoke an argument with him, but he had circumvented her.

She went into one Mexican shop to look around.   Near the edge of one table she found a piece of Mexican bric-a-brac, and picked it up.   Possibly she was nervous; at any rate the piece, a rather ugly ashtray, dropped to the floor and broke into small bits.

At once the owner of the store demanded payment.   She pretended she hadn't touched the ashtray, and said that she would not pay for it.   When the owner threatened to call the police, she said she'd call them herself.

She acted as if she were furious at the Mexican owner for

demanding payment. And the rest of us stood there, looking at her with horror, because we knew that as the result of her childish reactions, we might all land in a Mexican jail! One of the men in the party finally paid for the ashtray, a total charge of about one dollar.

You'll say: "That girl was nuts." And in a way she was. She was deliberately seeking trouble.

Not all of us go that far in our search for anger-provoking situations.

But what about the son who knows that his father hates the Democratic party, and deliberately brings up an argument about its merits?

What about the daughter who knows her mother thinks she is too strict with her children, and deliberately spanks them in front of grandmother? What about the grandfather who knows his son doesn't want him to feed the children cookies and candy, and who does it anyway? What about the husband who knows that his wife's pet hate is to see him smoking a big black cigar, and who puffs away at it just to spite her?

Undoubtedly, there are men and women who think they thrive on the excitement of arguments. They should ask themselves: "What is my unconscious mind trying to accomplish by wasting my energy in arguments?"

Why we get into these dangerous arguments. Sometimes, fearing failure, we unwittingly doom ourselves to what we fear by wasting the energy we need for success in futile, bitter arguments. Then we can say, "Of course I couldn't write that letter today" or "Of course I couldn't sell 100 umbrellas today. My wife made me so angry I wasn't fit to do anything."

We're telling the truth. We really weren't fit for any constructive use of our energies. But why, oh, why, did we destroy the energy we needed so badly?

If you have unconsciously been marshaling your energies for bigger and better fights, ask yourself: "What have these fights really accomplished?"

If they have accomplished anything, isn't there some way of achieving the same thing without knocking yourself out and injuring your health? Once in a while, righteous indignation may be called for. But as a rule what we term "righteous indignation" is just self-indulgence.

5. Try to "pray away" your anger. If you have sufficient faith, you should be able to avoid getting angry most of the time because your faith should give you understanding and tolerance of others.

Your neighbor is unpleasant? He has taken advantage of your generosity? You should try to forgive him.

The Lord's Prayer includes the famous lines: "Forgive us our trespasses as we forgive those that trespass against us."

This implies that if we want God to forgive us, we must forgive those who have hurt us. We are told to bless, not curse our enemies. This is more for our sake than theirs. If we hate them, we'll use up precious energy. Hate and anger use up lots more energy than love and calmness.

Frankly, it isn't easy to pray sincerely for those who say and do spiteful things. However, it will usually help keep us from growing angry if we stop to think: "If I were in his place, is it possible I would act as he does?" You may say to yourself: "I certainly wouldn't be that petty, that mean."

Maybe you wouldn't. You are *you*. And if your life has been one in which you have received and given love, you will rarely be tempted to do hateful things.

But isn't it possible that there is something in the background of this man who has done this rotten thing to you that would account for his bad behavior? Perhaps he's panicky. You can learn to feel sorry for him, instead of being angry at him. Pity for others will not drain your energy, the way hatred and anger do.

WHAT TO DO IF YOU GROW ANGRY

In spite of all your efforts to control your temper, there will be times when you grow angry anyway. What do you do then?

The important thing to remember is that anger has equipped you for *action*. It has given you enormous quantities of physical energy, and you might as well use some of it. Your brain may not be working well, but the strength in your legs and arms will amaze you.

You're ready for action. Then go!

Choose an activity that requires abundant energy. If you can go for a swim, do that. Or play golf. Whacking that little ball is a pleasant substitute for punching your boss in the nose, and it's much less detrimental to your career. Swimming or golfing will use some of the energy available. Or go for a walk. You should be able to walk three times as far as usual. Or go into the garden; grab your weeder or your trowel, and dig up all the weeds you can. Pretend they're your enemies.

If you have a home gym or belong to an athletic club or a boxing class, by all means take out your anger against a dummy.

If you've been needing wood for the woodpile, this is a perfect time for woodchopping.

If you're a homemaker, there never was a better time for spring cleaning. By the time you have cleaned two closets, gotten down on your knees to do the floors, and furiously pursued the dust lurking in the bedroom corners, you'll be blissfully exhausted instead of exhausted by anger. When you are blissfully exhausted you can sleep. When you are in the throes of anger, you can't. So you might as well try to exhaust yourself physically. After *physical* exhaustion, a night's rest can restore you to normal. On the other hand, *emotional* exhaustion through anger is apt to lead to a restless night, so that you will wake up tired the next morning.

Anger, particularly over trifles, is one of the worst enemies robbing you of precious vitality. If you must get angry, get angry over a rotten political deal, public vice, or the filth of the slums in your city. If you crusade against these things, your anger will at least *not* militate against your self-esteem.

When to anger, you have to add remorse for having made a donkey of yourself, you'll be so upset you won't have energy enough to do anything worth-while.

Let us repeat and remember the words of the Bible: "He that is slow to anger is better than the mighty; and he that ruleth his spirit than he that taketh a city."

IN A NUTSHELL:
FIVE WAYS TO KEEP FROM GETTING ANGRY

1. Study the way in which other individuals express their anger. Then decide you won't make that much of a donkey of yourself.

2. When you are tempted to become angry, think of the person who is being unpleasant as a fictional character. Try to describe him to yourself. This will help take your mind off your own injured feelings.

3. Talk as little as possible to an angry person, and in as low a voice as possible.

4. Try to avoid the kind of situations and discussions that are apt to lead to hot arguments.

5. Pray for the control of your temper.

HOW TO HANDLE ANGER WHEN IT HITS YOU

1. Try to channel your anger into constructive, crusading activities.

2. Engage in some strenuous physical activity.

Seven Ways to Reduce
Energy-Destroying Tension

ONE DAY AT A NATIONAL SALES EXECUTIVES CONFERENCE TO which I was invited as a reporter, I sat at lunch opposite a distinguished-looking sales executive. In the course of our conversation he told me about his hectic work week. For six days a week he worked all day at his office, and every night he entertained customers till the wee hours.

"How do you manage to do all that work without becoming exhausted and getting tied up in nervous knots?" I asked.

OUR GROWING DEPENDENCE ON PILLS

"The answer's very simple," he said. "Plenty of whiskey every night, and once a week a visit to my doctor. He says I have a tendency to become exhausted without knowing it. The injection he gives me each week is supposed to keep me from becoming over-tense."

This executive is not alone in his pitiful overdependence on liquor and pacifying shots.

Recent figures indicate that between 20,000,000 to 30,000,000 prescriptions for pacifying drugs were filled this past year in

97

the United States alone. That may very well mean that more
than 30 million individuals have taken the drugs; some foolishly pass their tranquilizers along to their friends as casually
as they'd offer them a piece of chewing gum or candy.

"We are becoming a nation of addicts," Dr. Benjamin Finesilver, former head of the department of neurology at Cedars of
Lebanon Hospital, told me.

"We are all potential addicts. Some Americans are addicted
to cigarettes, some to liquor, some to pacifying pills.

"I know that some of the literature devoted to tranquilizers
has claimed great benefits from their use.

"In properly selected and supervised cases, they have value,
but they are not panaceas. Certainly they are not the answer to all emotional and mental problems."

*Any therapy in which a patient has faith—even a sugar pill
—may be temporarily helpful.* "Once I prescribed five drops
of harmless vegetable coloring matter in a glass of water. The
patient, not knowing what was in the water, returned the following week to complain that the medicine was too strong,
and that she wanted something a bit weaker.

"Tranquilizers do not remove the basic causes of tensions.
At one psychiatric hospital conference I made the statement
that my experience with such drugs has been contrary to the
literature that is constantly pouring in on me. 'Which shall I
believe, gentlemen,' I asked, 'the literature I read or my own
observations?' "

The patient who was helped by looking at pills. "The doctors whom I addressed at another meeting thought I was kidding when I said I had a patient who had been helped by
looking at the pills. I was *not* kidding.

"She had had shock treatments, and had benefited from
them. After they were over, she and her family felt that she
needed a tranquilizer to help her keep calm. Believing that
a tranquilizer might be beneficial in this instance, I prescribed
100 tablets, to be taken at the rate of three a day.

"Each day her husband talked to me over the 'phone, and

reported to me how well his wife was doing. 'The pills are just great for her,' he said.

"I wanted to see her personally. After a month had elapsed, she came in to see me.

"She was doing very well. I asked her if she had been taking the tablets.

"She said yes, she carried the bottle with her all the time. Then she showed it to me. Actually, she had taken just about three tablets during the entire month. Knowing that she had them with her and could take them if she wished had been reassuring to her.

"Apparently just looking at the pills had helped her to stay relatively calm."

The individual who gets into the habit of taking tranquilizing pills so that he can face life's problems with equanimity may feel more cheerful for a while, but the problems remain, and his ability to solve them is not increased by the habitual use of the pills.

That is why Dr. Robert H. Felix, Director of the National Institute of Mental Health, says that he would never prescribe tranquilizing pills for anyone who simply has normal tensions to face, only for a man who is actually mentally ill. Certain of these drugs, he says, when given to a person who is not mentally ill, make him less alert and decrease his psychological and motor performance.

In general, doctors do not feel that the widespread use of tranquilizing pills is an unmixed blessing.

If pills are no panacea, what sort of protection against nervous tensions can we find?

Probably the best method of overcoming undue nervous tension is to discover the cause of our mental conflicts, and do our best to solve our problems as promptly as possible.

The basic cause of our troubles is often underneath our own skins. "The kingdom of heaven is within you," and so is the kingdom of mental hell. Every day in a hundred different ways, by the things we do, say, and think, each of us manufactures a little bit of heaven or hell for ourselves, and for those around us.

You can't live completely free of problems. This doesn't mean that it is ever possible to live in a mental world 100 per cent free of inner conflicts.

If our aged parents live in our homes and spoil our children, we'll be torn between wanting to put them into an old folks' home, wanting to change them, and wanting to make their last years comfortable. If a close relative asks us to lend him money to support a business we think is headed for the rocks, we'll be torn between wanting to help him and wanting to save our money. If we think an acquaintance is imposing on us by asking too big a favor, we may be torn between wanting to please him and wanting to avoid being exploited.

To expect to live completely free of problems is ridiculous. It's equally foolish to expect to live in such a way that we are never torn by doubts or nervous tensions.

But you can reduce tensions in your life. I can't and won't promise that either I or anyone else can eliminate them 100 per cent from your life. If you could get rid of them completely, you'd be foolish to. A reasonable, moderate amount of tension suitable in quantity and quality to the situations we are called upon to face in everyday life adds to our energy. We want to avoid abnormal tension only. Here are some methods that will help you reduce your own tensions, without resorting to pills.

SOME METHODS FOR REDUCING NERVOUS TENSION

1. Don't expect to be 100 per cent free of nervous tension

Says Dr. Benjamin Finesilver: "It is impossible, living in our current civilization, to be 100 per cent tension free. Only individuals devoid of sense and sensibility could live completely without tensions. If you had no sensations in your skin, lots of biting fleas wouldn't irritate you. If you had no mind and no feelings, you would not be disturbed by hunger, poverty, and frustration.

"If you have a mind and some feelings, you must expect to have some inner tensions."

Actually, why should any of us want to be 100 per cent free of nervous tension?

Probably our nervous tensions give us the drive to make something of ourselves. If Beethoven had been a calm, peaceful man, do you think he could have written his sublime melodies?

Dr. Benjamin Finesilver told me: "Anyone worth his salt who accomplishes anything in this world is neurotic to some degree. The great things in the world are not accomplished by passive, phlegmatic men, but by impulsive, aggressive neurotics."

2. Facing a serious conflict

Whenever you are faced with a serious conflict, take a course that leaves you feeling self-respect, rather than self-contempt.

In *Our Inner Conflicts* (New York: W. W. Norton & Company, Inc., 1945) Dr. Karen Horney tells the story of an engineer who often had spells of fatigue. He was working in collaboration with others, and he felt that his colleagues didn't give his opinions sufficient consideration. Once, when a decision was made during his absence, he was furious. No one had given him a chance to offer his suggestions.

"Under these circumstances," says Dr. Horney, "he could have regarded the procedure as unjust and put up a fight, or he could have accepted the majority decision with good grace. Either reaction would have been consistent. But he did neither. Though he felt deeply slighted, he did not fight. Consciously he was merely aware of being irritated. The murderous rage within him appeared only in his dreams. This repressed rage—a composite of his fury against the others and of his fury against himself for his own meekness—was

mainly responsible for his fatigue." (Pages 28–29). His
energies were bottled up inside him, causing fatigue and tension to take over.

Two conflicting tendencies. Dr. Horney's engineer wanted
to boss others, but this was combined with an abnormal need
for approval and affection. If he insisted on having his own
way, this engineer knew he'd make his colleagues dislike him.
On the other hand, when he was submissive, he hated himself.

The worst possible decision to make is to *appear* to accept
a situation you dislike, without mentally accepting it. Either
fight or give in, but don't try to straddle the fence.

Don't be over-meek. Like this engineer, you may think that
being over-meek and giving in to others will reduce your nervous tension. However, it will do so only if it leaves you glowing with a feeling of self-sacrifice, and this rarely happens,
since most of us were not born to be martyrs.

If we behave like Caspar Milquetoast in a situation where
we feel boldness of attitude is called for, we drain ourselves of
energy. Anything we do that results in self-contempt is always hard on our energy.

Decide whether the fight for a principle is worth-while; then,
if it is, fight. If it isn't, relax.

Always behave in a way that leaves you feeling a certain
amount of admiration for your own conduct. Or if that sounds
egotistical to you, try to behave in a manner that would win
your admiration if someone else behaved that way.

3. Don't try to live in the past or in the future

Actually, it is impossible to change the past, and foolish to
be too anxious about the future. Still, it is a common practice
to live on a trapeze suspended between a past that cannot be
changed and a future that cannot always be anticipated.

The word that can wreck your nervous energy. One little
word—*if*—can wreck your nervous energy. Many individuals
carry yesterday, today, and tomorrow with them, all at the
same time.

"If only I hadn't invested in that gold mine," sighs one
widow.

"If only I hadn't bought that penny uranium stock," sighs another.

"What an idiot I was to divorce my former husband," a friend of mine once told me. "I don't know what possessed me. Possibly I was just stupid and immature. When I realized what a mistake I had made, I wanted to rectify it, but it was too late. He had already married someone else, and she's smart enough to hang on to him. I wish I had been as wise. If only . . . ."

If all the "if onlys" sighed by unhappy men and women each day were laid side by side, we would more than fill the Congressional Library with books consisting of just two words, repeated over and over, "If only."

We might as well accept Omar Khayyam on this subject:

> The moving finger writes; and, having writ,
> Moves on: nor all your piety nor wit
> Shall lure it back to cancel half a line
> Nor all your tears wash out a word of it.

The "if only" discussion leads to quarrels. Often my husband and I have caught ourselves at this futile "if only" game. If, during the war, we had invested all our savings in blue chips instead of putting them into government bonds. . . . (At this point we forget that we were moved by patriotic motives more than by economic ones.) If only we hadn't sold a certain blue chip for a tiny profit, instead of the big profit we could have made if we'd held on. If only we hadn't gone into that business that soured on us.

From this beginning, it's only a step to "Who sold that good stock?" and "Who bought that bad one?" A quarrel would inevitably follow, if my husband at some point in this senseless discussion didn't put an end to it by imitating an owl. "Who? Who? Who?" he laughs. "Are we starting that again?"

So we stop, and try, as adults should, to live in the present.

We're all like customers in a supermarket. A brilliant woman, Margery Wilson, noted charm teacher and author, told a Beverly Hills audience recently: "I believe that we're all like the woman who goes shopping in the supermarket, wheeling her little cart in front of her, and taking down packages from the shelves. One day she makes up her mind to take down a package that might be labelled 'I'm going to be upset today' and in the package are anger, a fast beating heart, and a stomach upset."

How many of us take down the package labelled "Worry about the past" or "Regret for what is over"?

How to shop in the supermarket of life. The next time you go shopping in the supermarket of life, why not take down instead a package labelled "Courage and wisdom with which to solve today's problems"? Margery Wilson told me that each night before she retires, she puts a shopping list of the things she wants out of life beside her bed. Why not try it yourself?

How foolish to go shopping for "anxiety about tomorrow"! Biblical students assure us that the Bible's message, "Give no thought to the morrow" means "Have no anxiety about tomorrow."

In order to avoid unnecessary anxiety, do such sensible things as providing yourself with adequate insurance against fire, theft, ill health, and automobile accidents. When you know that the most serious contingencies can be met financially, you will have no need to be anxious about tomorrow.

How to prevent needless anxiety about the future. If you are taking out automobile insurance, the most important provisions are those protecting you against lawsuits if you damage someone else's car or other property or, heaven forbid, injure someone physically in an accident.

If you own your own home, liability insurance costing about $25 for three years will protect you against various kinds of possible lawsuits. Most mortgage companies insist on your carrying fire insurance. For your own protection, you should also carry extended insurance, which will usually provide for wind damage and other hazards.

Fortunately for most of us, employers are becoming more and more aware of the desirability of insurance safeguarding their employees in case of ill health. Hospital and surgery bills are difficult to estimate in advance, so the prudent man sees to it that such bills are provided for in advance by adequate insurance. If you can afford it, a very helpful type of illness insurance is the kind known as calamity insurance. The first hundred or two hundred or even five hundred dollars' worth of expense may be deducted from this type of insurance. It will pay the major part of the expense of calamitous illnesses costing thousands of dollars, for which it is otherwise difficult to provide in advance.

You should also provide yourself with certain types of emotional insurance. Besides financial insurance, you should also take out insurance against giving in to emotionally induced illness and fatigue due to emotional causes.

"In many cases," says Dr. Finesilver, "fatigue in both men and women has no physical cause." Why then do we so often go around feeling exhausted? Because we have suffered from negative, destructive, fatigue-producing emotions.

One of the most powerful forces in human nature is our imagination. The power of our imagination can be arrayed either for or against us. Actually imagination is a much greater force than so-called "will power."

We like to kid ourselves about how much will power we possess. Nevertheless, you couldn't so much as lift your hand by sheer will power, if your imagination were to tell you that it was *impossible* to lift that hand. This has been proven by a number of experiments in hypnosis.

When your imagination and your will power are engaged in a struggle with each other, your imagination will always win, since it is one of the most powerful forces in your internal artillery. To insure yourself against emotionally induced illness, you must learn to use this all-powerful force constructively. Used constructively, your imagination can produce an attitude that will help insure you against over-reacting to ordinary tensions.

Let us take two men, for instance, each facing the same situation. Both have invested heavily in the stock market. Along comes a fairly serious crash, and each finds that the current value of his holdings is about half of what it used to be.

One takes a forward-looking attitude. "I bought good

stocks," he says to himself. "Our economy is in good shape. There may be a recession, but eventually our economy will go forward, as it always has in the past. If I hold on, my stocks, which were well-chosen, will be worth more than I paid for them."

He's right. Even those who were hit by the 1929 crash, if they were not on margin, eventually saw their blue chips in most cases come back to higher prices than they originally paid for them.

The second man has adopted a tension-producing attitude. "Business is getting worse every year," he thinks gloomily. "The stock market will continue to go down indefinitely. We've had over ten years of prosperity. Now we'll probably have over ten years of depression."

He grows more and more panicky, until at the bottom of the crash, he sells all his holdings. A study of economics would have taught him that our country has always enjoyed more years of prosperity than years of adversity.

One type of insurance we should all take out is "reasonable optimism." In the long run, if we try to make intelligent decisions, most situations will work out quite well. I know a great many people who believe that everything happens for the best. Although this theory could be argued pro and con, it is a fact that many situations that look black at the time they happen turn out to have very happy final results. One can reasonably take the attitude that what may look like an unlucky stroke of fortune may eventually turn out to be the best thing that ever happened to us.

One woman I know was heartbroken when her husband, who had made her life miserable with his cruelty, left her. Normally, a woman who had been treated so badly might have reacted by saying, "The so and so. I should have left him years ago." But she confessed that once he was gone, she was filled with loneliness and self-pity. Finally, she consulted a psychiatrist.

"What makes you so sure that this isn't the beginning of a better life for you?" he asked her.

I am not, of course, arguing—and neither was he—that every

marriage in which there are some unpleasant factors should be dissolved by divorce. But when you are hit in the face by a situation that seems intolerable, how indeed can you be sure that in the long run this will not turn out to be an experience that starts you on a new and better life?

Six types of good emotional insurance. I don't think anyone has better defined the types of emotional insurance we should all take out than the late John Schindler, M.D., in *How To Live 365 Days a Year* (Prentice-Hall, Inc.: Englewood Cliffs, N. J., 1954, p. 90).

Says he: "Run these flags up on your masthead and keep them flying:

"Equanimity ('Let's stay calm.')

"Resignation ('Let's accept this setback gracefully.')

"Courage ('I can take this and more.')

"Determination ('I'll turn this defeat into victory.')

"Cheerfulness ('Bowed but not broken.')

"Pleasantness ('Still good will toward men.')"

These six types of emotional insurance will help us to face and vanquish most difficulties; they will keep our attitudes free of too much tension; they will enable us to smile, even in the face of unhappy situations.

Equanimity is important because every day we are going to be exposed to some problems, some hard knocks. Since all of us have some desires, we are bound to have some frustrations. But if we can't accustom ourselves to taking each little blow as it comes and rolling with the punch, how can we expect to be able to take devastating blows, if and when they do come along?

Why should any of us expect to be immune from occasional illness, tragedy, or heartache? Perhaps these challenges are presented to us because God thinks it is time we met them. Probably only by facing them realistically can we really grow up.

Until we become emotionally mature enough to handle our emotions wisely, we cannot expect to have enough energy to do anything worth-while.

For many of us, trust in His eternal wisdom is the only peace of mind insurance we can buy. How can we buy it? By confessing humbly to God: "I find it hard to believe, particularly when I am beset by troubles. Help Thou my unbelief."

4. Don't expect perfection of yourself or others

Harold J. Hoxie, M.D., doctor of internal medicine at Glendale Medical Center, Glendale, California, discovered that many of his patients made themselves ill by expecting to achieve perfection in everything they attempted. To help them, he worked out a set of principles for perfectionists.

One that I like very much is "Be dissatisfied enough to improve, but satisfied enough to be happy." He added, "Perfection is rarely attained, so be satisfied with less."

Jim was a junior executive who had to find this out for himself. He was being considered for a promotion. The new job would require him to do a great deal of entertaining. In his eagerness to get it, he decided to throw a really impressive party for his boss. He told his wife that every detail must be planned to perfection.

He was so tense about it himself, he made her tense. Loving her husband greatly and feeling that this party might help to decide his future, she planned it with meticulous care.

She worried about the guest list. Would all their guests like each other? Was her list complete? Wouldn't it be terrible if she made a mistake and failed to invite someone important to her husband?

She worried about the silver, the linens, the wines, the foods, the seating arrangements. Though she had a competent cook, she kept bustling into the kitchen, giving directions over and over again to the maid, who had heard her correctly the first time.

At the party, she just barely greeted the guests, then rushed frantically back and forth from kitchen to dining room supervising the arrangements.

In the meantime, her husband was an equally over-anxious host. Instead of making his guests comfortable, he made them aware of his anxiety. He flitted about so nervously that he gave the impression of being an over-solicitous head waiter instead of a host. In his zeal for perfection, he wore himself out, and made his guests almost as jittery as he was himself.

After the party was over, the executive the couple had been trying to impress discussed it with his wife.

"Do you think," he asked, "those two would ever fit into our picture, if we gave him a job where he had to entertain customers?"

The wife shook her head. "Good heavens, no," she said. "They tried so hard they made me feel fidgety. Can you imagine what they'd do to out-of-town buyers? They'd chase them away."

Of course the man didn't get the job. By trying too hard for perfection, he and his wife had made his guests feel ill at ease.

There are no perfect parties. Why should there be? Life itself isn't perfect. The host or hostess who regrets the fact that the food or the wines or the dessert didn't turn out quite as well as he had hoped is wasting energy on unnecessary regret.

A prominent executive told me, "Guests feel more comfortable with a host or hostess who enjoys their company, than with one who jumps to her feet every second, busying herself with a thousand small details, exhausting herself unnecessarily."

Trying to be a perfectionist is one of the most exhausting aims in the world. If you have a job to do that should be as perfect as possible, leave yourself plenty of time to do it. Also when it is completed, have someone look over the finished job.

Many years ago, I was assistant editor on a magazine, and used to read proofs as part of my job. When I was given the proofs of my own first book to read, I thought I would be 100 per cent accurate. Later, when the book was published, I discovered that my "eagle" eye had been far from perfect. I resolved that in the future I would allow friends as well as myself to look over proofs.

Realizing in advance that you will not be perfect in any respect prevents the bitter disappointment that disrupts energy.

5. Don't lead an invalid's life

There is a theory that overwork causes fatigue and rest always cures it. But that isn't necessarily true. Dr. Rex Hersey, the famous psychologist, once said that many individuals and families are tired because *they're not active enough.*

Some families have been cured just by *increasing* their activities.

One man said to an expert, "But I come home tired every night at six just from overwork. How can I possibly become less tired by doing more?"

"Just try three new activities three nights a week," the expert said.

The plan worked. Actually Mr. X wasn't tired, just bored. Too little activity will bore the pants off almost anyone.

In fact, some of the worst types of fatigue can be caused by inactivity. That was Tom's trouble.

The hypochondriac who suffered from fatigue. From boyhood, Tom had been brought up by a mother who implanted the idea in his consciousness that he was frail and very subject to fatigue. If he wanted to go out, and it was raining, she dutifully reminded him to take his rubbers, his umbrella, and his raincoat. If the rain was really coming down in sheets, she'd say, "But Tom, you'd better stay home. You're so frail, you're apt to catch pneumonia."

When he went to school, she discouraged him from attempting any athletic activities, and persuaded the family doctor to give him a note asking that he be excused from gym classes. When he was invited to parties or club meetings, she fearfully warned him against over-exerting himself.

When the war came along, she insisted that Tom would never be drafted; he was obviously too frail, too susceptible to illnesses. The Army Draft Board thought differently.

It took Tom years to overcome his mother's training. However, today, he is a healthy young man, but if it hadn't been for circumstances, he might still cherish the idea of himself as an invalid.

6. Have a philosophy of life that will give you more energy

Have a scale of values. Decide what's important, what's only relatively important, and what is unimportant. Just as you wouldn't pay $300 for a suit worth only $100, never use up $300 in energy for something worth only $100 of your vitality.

Obviously the importance of a task can rarely be measured in exact financial terms. However, it is ridiculous to give a huge part of your energy to something that you yourself, after due thought, regard as relatively unimportant.

It's vital for all of us to learn to distinguish in our own minds between things that do count and those that don't. Never pay more emotionally for anything than it is worth. You pay in loss of energy and sometimes even in loss of health because of others' pettiness, but only if you let that pettiness affect you.

Never let a stupid insult upset you. Once a charming woman I know was insulted by a man who, in a fit of anger because she had been promoted over his head, abused her in guttersnipe language.

For a moment she was furious. Then she decided that it didn't matter what he said, as long as she knew it wasn't true. After all, she realized he was acting out of malice and anger, so what difference did it make what he called her?

When others slight you or call you names you don't deserve, let your sense of humor and your knowledge of human nature come to the fore. Such individuals are often pitiable; if we could look into their hearts, we would feel sorry for them, instead of resenting their torrid language.

YOU CAN CONTROL YOUR THOUGHTS

7. Think positive but realistic thoughts

As part of your philosophy, realize that you can control your thoughts, as long as you are mentally healthy. And you will remain mentally healthy if you practice positive but realistic thinking.

Make constructive suggestions to yourself daily. But don't make them so all-inclusive that your rational mind will laugh at them. For instance, Coué's formula, "Every day in every way I am getting better and better" worked for those who were not analytical. But it couldn't work for anyone who said to himself, "But that's ridiculous. The pain in my big toe is not getting any better; I've never learned to control my temper, and my headaches are not vanishing."

Positive affirmations are fine, but they must be keyed to one's realistic expectations.

"This will pass" is more realistic than "Everything is getting more wonderful every minute." The unconscious mind will accept "I am going to sleep well, and wake up feeling fine tomorrow morning" sooner than it will accept "I am going to sleep well every night of my life."

Give the unconscious mind positive thoughts to chew on, but don't give it unrealistic thoughts that the conscious mind refuses to swallow.

You and you alone control your real thoughts. Thieves may break down your doors and enter your house, and steal your possessions. But you are always safe in your innermost thoughts. No matter what life does to you, you can control them.*

The man who learned to be happy. Gamaliel Bradford, the famous biographer, once said that he would have spared himself many years of suffering if he had known in his youth the lesson he learned much later: that he could think about anything he wanted to, and dismiss all thoughts that irked him from his mind. You can learn this lesson today, right this instant.

Let us remember what Alfred Loomis said: "I am bigger than anything that can happen to me. All these things—sor-

---

* For an excellent explanation of the power of your own mind and thoughts over your life and good health, see *Your Mind Can Make You Sick Or Well,* by Wachtel (Englewood Cliffs, N.J.: Prentice-Hall, Inc., 1959).

row, misfortune, and suffering—are outside my door. I am in the house, and I have the key. "

POINTERS TO REMEMBER

1. Don't expect to be 100 per cent free of nervous tensions.

2. When you have a choice to make, always choose a course of action that will leave you feeling proud of yourself, or at least not ashamed.

3. Live in the present, not in the past or in the future.

4. Don't expect perfection of yourself or others.

5. Don't lead an invalid's life if you are not an invalid.

6. Decide what's important, what's relatively important, and what's unimportant, and distribute your nervous energy accordingly.

7. Give your mind positive thoughts to chew on but keep them realistic. You can control your thoughts, and your thoughts control your life.

8

How to Conquer the Worry Habit That Destroys Energy

IN A LARGE AMERICAN CITY THERE WAS A PROPHETESS WHO called all her followers together and told them, "Next Wednesday the world will be destroyed by fire and flame. Between now and then you have time to flee from this city, and go to the mountain top nearby, which God will preserve from all harm. Before you leave, give away or sell all your possessions, and we shall start a new community on that mountain."

Her followers, filled with fear and worried about the coming destruction of the world, sold or gave away their possessions, then gave the money to the prophetess to use in starting their new community. Then they all went to the mountain, where they awaited the end of the world.

Wednesday came and went, and nothing happened.

Angry and perplexed, they sought out the prophetess and demanded an explanation of why none of her prophecies had come true.

"It's very simple," she said grandly. "My Wednesday is not your Wednesday."

Fake prophets appeal to abnormal worriers. Throughout the history of the world, there have been many similar false prophets and prophetesses. Many of them have been be-

114

lieved, because their predictions have appealed to minds with
abnormal fears and worries.

We live in an age of anxiety.   Most of us would not fall for
such gloomy predictions, yet we can't deny that we are all living in what the psychiatrists call an "age of anxiety."   Too
many of us are worry warts.   Living in the shadow of the
atomic age, we are afraid of living, and afraid of dying.   We
fear war; we fear the destruction of our cities by the strange
new weapons; and we fear poverty.   Along with our fears
about Russia's ability to outpace us in some military directions,
come great personal fears and anxieties.

The shadow of atomic death hangs over our heads.   It is a
mere shadow, but we are afraid of our shadows.   We are also
concerned with whether or not we can hold our jobs, meet all
our expenses on what we're making and perhaps save a little
for the future, and stay healthy through all the emotional
strains and stresses of modern life.   Then, on top of all this, we
sometimes worry about the impression we make on others.
We know that how we impress others may make a difference,
not only socially but also in business.   And so we are apt to
worry about whether we are saying too much or too little,
and in a business deal, whether we are asking for too much or
too little.

Unnecessary fears and worries waste our energies.   Fear
takes a thousand forms.   Each time we feel fear, our bodies
are fortified for action, just as they are by anger.   Like anger,
fear is in most cases a spendthrift emotion.   Dr. Joseph F.
Montague pointed out: "Fear certainly is the most powerful
stimulus known and even if no action appears to result, it
draws away nervous energy and produces exhaustion."

Needless worry can destroy your health.   Needless worry—
the kind that makes your thoughts go round and round like a
trapped squirrel in a cage—can not only make you chronically
tired, but it can also destroy your health.

In *Stop Worrying and Get Well*, Edward Podolsky, M.D.
(New York: Bernard Ackerman, Incorporated, revised, 1944)
shows how worrying can help cause the following illnesses:

angina pectoris (a form of heart ailment), irritable heart (with pain, sweating, flushes, and other nervous manifestations), asthma, dyspepsia, stomach ulcers, mucous colitis, ulcerative colitis, tooth decay, acute eczema, high blood pressure, rheumatism, colds, hysterical blindness, and thyroid trouble.

The intense emotional suffering associated with chronic worrying can even help cause diabetes, says Dr. Podolsky.

When you are worried, he explains, the blood pressure rises, the heart beats fast, and sugar appears in the urine. For emergencies, these results give you greater energy. "More sugar in the system means more energy to get away from a fire, an earthquake, or an airplane raid." But how often do you have to escape from such dangers?

If you get panicky when panic isn't called for, and your body is frequently called upon to deliver more energy than you need, it will suffer. "The sugar will not disappear; it will remain. Instead of a transient glycosuria (sugar in the urine) we have a permanent one, and that, of course, means diabetes" (*Stop Worrying and Get Well*, page 98).

But we cannot live completely worry-free. Should we be like the "brave" creatures of Aldous Huxley's *Brave New World* who could wipe out all worries just by taking the right pills?

Psychiatrists say no, a thousand times no!

To be completely unworried may be a sign of mental illness. Says Dr. Judd Marmor, M.D., noted Beverly Hills, California, psychoanalyst: "In the past 20 years, psychiatrists have come to an awareness of the fact that fear, under realistic conditions of danger, is a normal reaction of the healthy ego. This realization was of enormous help in strengthening the morale of World War II soldiers, who by learning to accept their fear as normal, were relieved of the additional burdens of guilt and self-condemnation which characterized their predecessors in World War I.

"I believe it is equally important for psychiatrists to recognize the normalcy of realistic worry, and am of the opinion that the mental hygiene value of such recognition, just as in the case of fear, can be extremely valuable to the public at large. One is impressed by how many people operate upon the assumption that to worry about anything is ipso facto 'neurotic,' and that the 'normal' person should never worry. Most people apparently seem to be unaware of the rather obvious fact that to be unworried in the face of a distressing or threatening reality situation may sometimes be a symptom of a serious mental disorder, rather than a sign of mental health."

A certain amount of realistic worry is normal. Dr. Marmor feels that the problem with which we must be concerned is not the fact that worry exists, but rather the question of whether it has a realistic basis, and whether it leads ultimately to some mentally healthy action or thought.

For instance, Mr. Jones may be worried because his daughter, Mabel, has become infatuated with a man who has had three nervous breakdowns. He is realistically afraid that this man may be of an unstable temperament, and worried for fear that his daughter will elope with him.

The daughter is a romanticist who believes that all her fiancé needs is the traditional love of a good woman. Her father doubts if this neurotic young man will be able to face the challenges of marriage, and the responsibility of supporting a young wife.

Mr. Jones has reasonable grounds for his worry, and he is a normal, not a neurotic, father because he worries in this instance. If he takes a sensible, constructive step to help Mabel see her problems in a more realistic light, he has probably done all that can be done in this particular situation. Perhaps he can get the young man's permission to discuss the matter with the psychiatrist who took care of him during his previous breakdowns. If the boy really has the girl's welfare at heart, he will want a psychiatric opinion on his readiness for marriage. If at this point he refuses to talk to his psychiatrist, the girl's father has a legitimate right to be worried.

There is nothing wrong about worrying, provided we worry sanely and realistically, and seek realistic solutions.

The purpose of this chapter is to help you find your own realistic solutions for your own worries.

TEN WAYS TO ELIMINATE UNDESIRABLE WORRYING

1. Sort your worries

Write down on a sheet of paper the exact nature of your worries. If you cannot name your worry, but are filled with vague, mysterious fears, then you may have to consult a psychiatrist. But if your worries can be named, they can be faced.

Next to each worry, put down the answers to these questions: Is this problem one I can solve? What are the possible solutions?

Write down all the alternatives, and their possible effects. You must distinguish between problems that can be solved and those that can't, so that your energies can be channeled into finding practical solutions. They must not be wasted in thinking in a circle about problems that defy solution, like the incurable disease of a loved one.

2. Find a substitute

Find a substitute for the energy you are using on worrisome problems for which you cannot find a solution.

Let us say, for instance, that your father is dying of an incurable disease. You have consulted the best doctors available, but they give you no hope.

You must find some outlet for the energy you have been pouring into futile worrying. If you will undertake a job that requires every last ounce of your attention, you will not be able to concentrate so thoroughly on your worries.

The mind can dwell on only one thought at a time. Keep it so busy with a task you set yourself; be so inexorable in compelling yourself to finish this task that your worries will not oppress you as constantly as they otherwise would. This is a constructive use for your energy; the habit of worrying is a destructive, wasteful method of handling your God-given energies. It is particularly destructive when all you can do is bang your head against a stone wall.

A widow very much worried about the investments her husband has left her, because she has no information as to which ones she should keep, can, after the first shock of grief, take her mind off her troubles by consulting with experts about them, and by studying books on how to judge investments. At any stockbroker's office, she can consult reports about each individual company, and learn to judge whether the price of a stock is approximately right, in view of its earnings, past and potential.

A man who is worried about the fact that he is spending more than he makes should sit down with his wife and figure out a sensible budget. Or they might have a family consultation on how to make extra money to meet their mounting expenses.

In one family I know, even the children figured out a way of meeting their problems instead of worrying about them. Naturally they were grief stricken when their father died. But there were practical problems to think about, too. The insurance he left wasn't enough to cover their previous clothes allowance. Instead of worrying about how they could possibly compete with their classmates, coming to class in dowdy clothes, the children in the household—a 13-year-old boy and a 15-year-old girl—pitched in and sold birthday cards, Christmas cards, and novelties. The commissions they earned were about three times what their clothes allowances had formerly been.

However, when a tragic situation arises that permits no personal solution, then you can sometimes compensate for grief and heartache by throwing yourself into a community project. Thus a doctor who knows that he is ill with an incurable cancer may devote the rest of his life to research on the illness that has brought his own hopes to an end. A woman who lost her own child in a traffic accident due to bad traffic laws in her city devoted herself for years after her tragic loss to campaigning for better laws.

3. Accept "little worries" of life philosophically

Never give a ten cent problem a dollar's worth of worry. By learning to take your minor problems philosophically, you will be building up the stamina to face more serious problems.

If you don't learn to do this, you will not only waste energy; you will live in a continual fog, through which you will be unable to see the sources that could make you a happy human being.

One acquaintance of mine worried constantly because he was afraid that some of the units in a 12-unit apartment house he owned might become vacant. Actually, he was earning a good living at the time, and could have gotten along very well even if a couple of apartments had been vacated.

Imbued with the habit of worried thinking, he worried when all the apartments were full, for fear that a tenant might move out. When an apartment became vacant, he worried that a great deal of time might elapse before he found another tenant.

He didn't concentrate on happiness till he lost it. Two years later, when one of his children became ill with a potentially fatal disease, he said regretfully, "To think that two years ago I was carrying on about the fact that an apartment had become vacant. I didn't know enough to enjoy my happiness when I had it. Now it is only a memory. How I wish I could go back to those days!"

None of us can go back in time even two minutes; but we can appreciate what we have *while* we have it, and thank God for our blessings. When *little* things go wrong, we can maintain a calm unworried serenity, so that our energy is free to fight the more urgent problems in our lives, instead of being wasted on trivialities.

4. Learn to make decisions promptly

Making and unmaking the same decision can have disastrous effects upon your energy. It leaves you in a continual stew.

Once you have made up your mind, never change it unless you discover new facts that put the situation in a new light. Don't get into the habit of asking a dozen different individuals what they would do in your place. You will only become confused.

Unless the decision requires expert opinion, concentrate on digging up facts, not arraying opinions on one side or the other. For instance, suppose you are wondering whether to give up your job to try to find one in a different field. If you asked a dozen individuals what they would do, each one would decide the problem according to *his* personality. So don't waste your time rounding up their opinions. Better use that same energy constructively to find out what other jobs are available, whether you have the requirements for them, and whether they offer any advantages to you over your present position.

If you have trouble making decisions, compel yourself to make some every day. Solve one problem today, two tomorrow, three the next day.

It used to be a standing joke among my friends that I couldn't make up my mind about the most insignificant details of living. Should I have an omelette for lunch or a Caesar salad? Should I buy a friend a compact or something for her home?

Christmas shopping used to be an ordeal for me, because I just couldn't make up my mind.

As I related it in *Family Circle* magazine (September 1957), I was finally cured by following two bits of advice. "One came from a friend who pointed out that the great American psychologist and philosopher, William James, said it is better to take *any* action—right or wrong—than to worry, fret and stew interminably. Action, James pointed out, is positive; worry is negative.

"The second piece of advice came from a charming character called Chatterer the Red Squirrel in one of Thorton W. Burgess's nature stories. Says Chatterer:

'Though right or wrong, you're bound to find
Relief in making up your mind.' "

You are also going to find a tremendous liberation of energy. It is as though making up your mind releases a great flow of blood sugar, readying you for action. Your unconscious mind says to your conscious one: "Go! Go! Go!" or "Act! Act! Act!"

Have you ever seen one of those submarine pictures where the captain suddenly shouts orders at the crew, and they all man their guns or do whatever submarine crews are supposed to do? That's the way it is when you reach a decision.

You can feel just like the captain, for all the forces in your body begin to work harmoniously, for the same purpose. Actually, once you make up your mind, you find that you have a wonderful crew: glands that pour forth just the hormones you need; blood that circulates to just the right places in your body for your needs; a new brain and an old brain that work beautifully together so long as you don't give them conflicting orders.

5. Rise above worries

Worries can be considered challenges. A famous tennis player whose knowledge of the game was fantastic kept losing games. Finally she had to consult a psychiatrist, who discovered that she always gave up when the going got rough.

He taught her to relax, to think of herself as a person who *could* rise above any obstacle. He also taught her to compensate for her unconscious desire to be weak. Whenever the game became truly rough, she was to call on her reserve energies. Normally, the worry-prone person *wastes* these energies in worrying.

Worry without action consumes much more energy than dynamic action without much worry.

For instance, there was a middle-aged man who was deeply worried when he learned that he had a minor heart illness. In his own mind he magnified this minor problem into an obsession. He told himself that the doctor was making light of his problem, in order not to frighten him, that he was much more ill than the physician would admit. He convinced himself that he just wouldn't be able to work and support his wife and two daughters. Nothing his doctor could say would reassure him.

Finally, he saw a psychiatrist, who pointed out that all his life he had resented the fact that he had to work so hard to make a living. Because of that resentment he was using his minor heart affliction as an excuse to get out of work.

This got him so angry that he went back to work. Twenty years have passed since then, and he is as healthy as any man I know.

A combination of worry and resentment had turned him into a weakling. When he was told that he was deliberately evading work, he was filled with the determination to prove that the psychiatrist was wrong.

Wishing to prove someone wrong often infuses us with extra energy. When self-respecting action, such as going back to work, is substituted for worry, we feel stronger; energy seems to flow into our veins; our lives are transformed.

6. Practice worrying 15 minutes a day

Whenever you are worried, jot down your worry on a sheet of paper. When you have collected several sheets, set a specific time, let us say from 5 to 5:15 P.M. each night, for worrying. Do your best to worry during that period. When you have spent 15 minutes harping on your worries, your mind will be so fed up on this ridiculous procedure, that you may begin to feel like doing something constructive. When you have finished your 15 minute period of worry, take your sheets of paper, and burn them in the fireplace.

7. List your current worries

Make a notation on your calendar pad, on the page set aside for a month from today, of your most severe current worries.

Today, do everything you can to solve them. When you have done all that you can, try to forget them.

A month from now, check the notation, to see how many of your worries remain. It is astonishing how trivial today's worries will often appear in the light of tomorrow's events.

A man who was terribly worried about a lingering illness decided that his worry was due to the fact that he wasn't satisfied with the doctor who was taking care of him. Making inquiries among his friends, he learned of another doctor, a specialist in such matters, who had helped one of his friends. As soon as he got in touch with the specialist, he felt his worries fading. Something about the specialist inspired his faith and confidence.

Within a month's time, he was on the road to recovery. Most problems, when tackled in this manner, will lead to a solution. Just ask yourself: What is my worry? Why am I worried? What can I do about it?

8. Be venturesome

An industrial engineer once stated that the timid mind is the tense, fatigued one. There are times when decisions must be made, even before all the facts are in. Under such circumstances, how can you be expected to be 100 per cent right in making them?

Don't expect it of yourself. This perfectionist aim is enough to drive anyone into a state of chronic worry and loss of energy through worry.

A wise businessman once suggested that the difference between success and failure is the difference between being right 48 per cent of the time and being right 52 per cent of the time. So why expect to be 100 per cent right? Take a few chances.

We often believe incorrectly that the meek, the frightened and the cowardly will make fewer mistakes than the brave and the venturesome.

This is false. Refusing to make a decision *is* a decision. You cannot run away from important decisions. If a woman decides to put up with her husband's cruelty and abuse without protesting, because she is afraid of losing him, she *has* already made her decision. For fear of what *might* happen if she protested against his sadism, she is making sure that what will happen will continue to be unpleasant.

The meek don't inherit the earth. Many have been misled by the Biblical saying, "The meek shall inherit the earth." We have a silly vision of the earth being inherited by those who let others kick them around, because they're worried about the effects of standing up for their principles.

The Greek word that was translated as "meek" didn't mean anything of this sort in Biblical times. The Abingdon Biblical

Commentary tells us that it meant the iron hand in the velvet glove. If you were meek, you walked humbly with your God; you were self-controlled and slow to anger—but if there was a good reason for getting angry, you didn't behave like Caspar Milquetoast.

Neither in heaven nor on earth can we expect those who allow others to walk all over them to inherit anything. Those who discipline themselves, so that the amount of energy they expend on worry is always justified by the cause, and always leads to constructive *action*, will inherit whatever they truly want on earth.

9. Be relaxed

The greatest authorities on relaxation say we cannot worry unduly if we relax *physically*. This means relaxing the large muscles in our arms and legs, the muscles in our necks, which become very tense when we worry, straightening out the worry frowns in our foreheads, and when we lie down to rest, the muscles in our eyes.

Watch what the worried person does: how he frowns, how tense his body gets, how he clenches his fist. Do the opposite.

In order to worry, you have to put forth excessive effort, the kind that produces a frown in your forehead, drooping muscles near your mouth, tense lines in your neck. Examine your face in a mirror when you worry; deliberately exaggerate those signs of worry; then wipe them out. Wipe out the muscular effort of worrying, and you often wipe out the worry.

The tension of your muscles in excessive worry causes great streams of energy to be wasted. Stop letting your energy go down those useless streams.

In learning to relax, lie down for a few minutes (perhaps 15 minutes to half an hour) every day, but don't overdo this by sleeping away half the day.

Try to learn the secret of differential relaxation. Don't let the phrase scare you away. All it really means is using *only* those muscles you actually need to accomplish anything, and relaxing all other muscles. A consulting psychologist of my acquaintance once met Eleanor Roosevelt and asked her how she managed to keep up her extraordinary schedule of activities without collapsing.

"Whenever I'm doing anything," she said, "I relax all muscles except those I absolutely have to use. Even when I read on a train or plane, I do so in such a relaxed position that anyone seeing me would imagine I was half asleep, maybe even drunk."

That is because Mrs. Roosevelt has learned the secret of using only those muscles that have to be used. Most of us tense up, and use a lot of unnecessary muscular power on almost everything we do. We assume that worry produces tension, but some wise psychologists warn us that muscular tension also produces worry.

Don't waste your priceless energy by too much resting. A certain amount of rest will build up your energy, but the moment you find yourself stewing about something, jump to your feet.

Fatigue can be a silent confession of an unwillingness to play the exciting part you're meant to play in life. A young woman I know confessed that once, as an Army wife, she had to spend months in a strange town. Unaccustomed to turning strangers into friends, she was afraid to leave her apartment in town in order to meet the other Army wives. She was afraid of what they would think of her if she made the first friendly gesture.

Instead of compelling herself to knock on some other wife's door, she ran away from her problem by spending almost three quarters of her day sleeping.

Like this Army housewife, each day when we awake we have a choice to make between having energy and not having it, between being fully alive or half dead.

She chose to be a Zombie during those months. Rather than make the effort of seeking out her neighbors, she retired to the privacy of her bedroom. Her concern about what her neighbors would think of her if she were mildly aggressive turned her into a fatigued, unhappy woman.

Like many others who are afraid to face life, she chose for a time to spend three quarters of her days in a horizontal position. This position may be great on the psychoanalyst's couch, but is easily overdone when used as an escape from facing problems. When we're on our feet, most of us know we must cope with life. When we do too much "bed resting," we may be indicating our eagerness to evade our waking problems.

Get out of that horizontal position early in the morning, and never get into it again when you are in a weepy, self-pitying mood. Something about the position makes self-pitiers wallow in their self-pity.

If you must worry excessively, try to worry on your feet! It's more apt to lead to action, which is healthier than stewing in your own juice.

10. Substitute another constructive habit for the destructive habit of worry

Worrying over every trivial thing can and usually does become a habit. Realizing this, a group of doctors in Boston organized the Thought Control Class at the Boston Dispensary. To this class came men and women from all over the country, whose doctors had examined them thoroughly, only to discover that they were ill and lacking in energy not for any physical reasons, but merely because they were worried.

Said one of these doctors to a group of professional worriers: "All of us have reservoirs of unseen power with which we can control our thinking . . . We cannot always prevent worried thoughts from entering our minds, but we can prevent them from staying there. You cannot keep the birds from flying overhead, but you can keep them from setting up nests in your hair. In the same way, your worried thoughts may sometimes clamor for admission into your mind, but chase them away, just as though they were bats trying to enter your house."

The best way to keep anxious thoughts from staying in your mind is to substitute pleasant thoughts for them. Of course, this doesn't mean that if you have a lump on your breast you should think of something beautiful in nature, so you won't have to concentrate on the sad thought that this might be cancer.

But it must be remembered that this group had nothing wrong with them physically. To make sure that the same thing is true of you, you must have your annual physical examination. If you have serious physical symptoms, see your doctor instead of relying on pleasant thoughts.

However, if your problem is not physical but consists of regret for a mistake made in the past or something of the sort, banish the thought.

At the Thought Control Class, patients were asked to picture a smooth lake in the wilderness in the warm summertime at about two in the afternoon, with no winds blowing, not a ripple on the lake.

"For thirty seconds," said the doctor, "see that quiet lake. Imagine its shining, serene surface. Then think of your mind as being as smooth, as unruffled by worries as that calm, cool lake."

The patients there learned to establish enough thought control to keep their minds and spirits unruffled.

So can you. And when you do, watch that energy rip forth from you! For as Edwin Markham, the poet, said once: "At the heart of the cyclone tearing the sky is a place of central calm."

Commented Dr. Norman Vincent Peale (*A Guide to Confident Living:* Englewood Cliffs, N.J.: Prentice-Hall, Inc., 1948): "The cyclone derives its power from a calm center. So does a man. Out of relaxation comes driving energy. Power is generated in and derived from a calm center."

TEN WAYS TO CONQUER THE HABIT OF WORRYING EXCESSIVELY OR UNNECESSARILY

1. Sort the worries that can be solved from the ones that can't. Write down possible alternative solutions for the ones that can be solved.

2. *Find a substitute (possibly hard work) for the energy you are using on worrisome problems for which you cannot find a solution.*

3. *Learn to take the little worries philosophically.*

4. *Learn to make decisions promptly.*

5. *Regard yourself as a person who can rise above worries.*

6. *Practice worrying 15 minutes a day, concentrating on worries you have written down on a sheet of paper. Then burn the sheet.*

7. *Note on your calendar pad, on the date a month from to-day, what your current worries are. Take steps today toward solving them. A month from today, check them to see how many of them still remain to plague you. Were they worth worrying about?*

8. *Be venturesome. Don't try to be 100 per cent right all the time, because it is impossible.*

9. *Be relaxed physically. Learn to relax every muscle in your body, particularly those muscles you have a tendency to tense when you worry.*

10. *Substitute a constructive habit for the destructive habit of worry.*

Part 3

HOW TO SPEND YOUR ENERGY WISELY

9

Stop Squandering Your Energy on Unnecessary Guilt Feelings

*I*T IS ALMOST IMPOSSIBLE FOR A CIVILIZED HUMAN BEING TO GO through life without sometimes having guilt feelings.

Such emotions are one of the greatest causes of fatigue. Dr. John Sutherland Bonnell, pastor of the Fifth Avenue Presbyterian Church in New York City, said recently, "Americans are the most tired people on earth. We work less but worry more than anyone else, largely as the result of our unresolved guilt."

There are two kinds of guilt feelings. Dr. Bonnell wisely distinguished between two types of guilt feelings: those based on a real offense against morals, and those pangs caused by a disturbed mind. "Help for real guilt," he said, "is the exclusive field of the minister." The mission of the psychiatrist, he added, is to deal with irrational, abnormal guilt feelings.

This distinction is important. When we suffer normal emotions of remorse, the amount of guilt felt is in proportion to the offense. We are conscious of the real cause of our feelings.

For instance, one man I know discovered, on leaving a supermarket, that he had accepted change for $20, though he had given the cashier only $10. When he realized that the cashier would have to make up the shortage out of her own salary, his conscience plagued him. Finally he went back to the store, where he returned the $10 he had wrongfully accepted. This freed him of his guilt feeling.

No sensible psychiatrist would consider his remorse abnormal. It is a normal price to pay for a normal kind of conscience.

The solution for such obvious offenses against our own inner standards is to make restitution when possible. If you feel you've done something wrong, do your best to rectify it, as quickly as possible. Your guilt feeling should then disappear.

Unresolved guilt will fester. Even if you try to dismiss the thought from your mind, it will bother you.

For example, recently in Los Angeles an unknown offender, plagued by his conscience, sent $120 to the police department to cover two thefts he had committed many years previously from two stores at which he had worked. From one he had stolen $25, from the other $35. He anonymously returned twice the amount he had stolen, in order to satisfy his own conscience. If the owners of the two stores could not be located, he asked that the money be given to charity. Actually so many years had passed that no one could locate them, and the money went to the policemen's charity fund.

One can readily imagine how through the years the offender's regret for what he had done had been a sore spot in his mind. Remorse of this type can make anyone less energetic, for the energy that should be going into constructive work goes into remorse.

If you contemplate violating your own conscience, it may punish you excessively. Dr. Benjamin Finesilver, well-known neuropsychiatrist practicing in Beverly Hills, California, told me: "Many decent and responsible men and women have a need for social approval and self-esteem, and are apt to suffer guilt feelings if they violate their own standards, or sometimes even if they contemplate violating them.

"Psychiatrists are not clergymen and our purpose is not to moralize, but to help patients reach a solution that will not hurt them or anyone else."

A widow of 35 came to Dr. Finesilver and explained that her life was truly miserable. She was constantly fatigued, and could hardly get up enough energy to take care of her small apartment.

She had been contemplating having an affair with a married man to whom she was attracted. But her conscience warned her that if she went ahead, she might destroy her peace of mind.

She was wasting a tremendous amount of energy on her inner battle. No wonder she had very little energy left for work!

"Under these circumstances," Dr. Finesilver said, "you certainly shouldn't have an extra-marital affair. The mere contemplation of an affair leaves you feeling guilty, because you might hurt an innocent wife. If you disobey your conscience, you might become the victim of even more crucifying guilt feelings."

Dr. Finesilver explained: "If a woman with a conscience has an affair of that type, she is in danger of later going into a depression or finding some other means of punishing herself.

"The test for any individual might be: 'What would I think of myself after doing this?' For a man or woman with a need for self-esteem, the fact that a certain act would destroy much of his self-respect should warn him against committing that act."

The extent and depth of our guilt feelings will often depend not so much on what we have done, as on how thick or thin-skinned we ourselves are.

Guilt feelings are sometimes out of proportion to their apparent cause. "There was a patient who was driving himself crazy with the thought that he had once killed a butterfly," said Dr. Finesilver. "When an individual reacts out of such proportion to the stimulus that produced the tension, we have a very serious mental condition to contend with."

This patient had a psychotic type of depression. You and I, as laymen, would probably say that he had a few buttons missing. He required a different type of treatment than the average neurotic.

In this particular case, shock treatment was indicated and given, in addition to other psychotherapy.

Abnormal guilt feelings are often associated with the death of those who have been very close to us. Serious depressions sometimes follow the death of someone who has been close to us. Dr. Erich Lindemann, the eminent psychiatrist, has pointed out that hidden feelings of hatred are sometimes responsible for overwhelming, abnormal grief over the death of a parent or a former mate.

For instance, let's take the case of Charles. When Charles' father died, Charles took it very hard. For months afterwards he went around like a pale shadow of himself, unable to sleep nights, or to work during the day. He was chronically fatigued.

Only a psychiatrist is qualified to determine the proper method of treating so serious a case, and Charles finally saw one.

To the psychiatrist, Charles' overwhelming grief, surpassing any normal emotional reaction to a parent's death, was a sign of a deep unconscious feeling.

Months of probing followed during which the psychiatrist helped Charles discover the core of his trouble.

The unconscious conscience that caused fatigue. Charles' excessive fatigue was caused by guilt feelings. From early childhood, he had secretly hated his father, who was stern and sometimes brutal with him. Hating him so much, he had often wished him dead.

When his father died, the stern unconscious conscience (called "the superego" by Freud) stepped in. "See what you've done," it screamed. "You've murdered your father."

Actually his father had died of completely natural causes.

But the unconscious conscience knows nothing of reason. Its constant accusations had overwhelmed Charles.

Charles gained new energy by overcoming unnecessary guilt feelings. After Charles became conscious of the real cause of

his devastating fatigue, he was able to get better with the help
of his psychiatrist.   His rational, conscious mind knew that he
wasn't guilty of his father's death.   The psychiatrist pointed
out that his fatigue was due to an unconscious, completely il-
logical belief in a connection between his childhood wish for
his father's death and the actual event.   Charles' tyrannical
unconscious conscience ceased to persecute him as soon as he
recognized that his sense of guilt was unreal.   After that, his
energy was restored to him.

Today, Charles, freed of most of his unnecessary guilt feelings, is back at work, happy and prosperous.   He has all the
energy he needs to carry on a difficult executive job.

FOUR WAYS TO AVOID EXAGGERATED
GUILT FEELINGS

1. Live up to your own conscience

Do not let others high pressure you into following a course
of conduct that goes against your grain.

Let us assume first of all that you have a reasonable conscience.   If it is normal, it will warn you against doing things
that go against your personal principles.   Actually, our consciences *should* protect us against making mistakes that will
make us miserable later.

Sometimes, however, we let ourselves be talked by others
into violating our own basic principles.

For instance, John was a conscientious man who tried each
year to turn in an honest income tax report.   When his neighbor Tom discovered that John reported his church contributions truthfully, he laughed at him.   "After all," he said, "if you
put 25 cents a week into the collection box and claim you put
in $2.00, who's to know the difference?   Why not claim a
bigger deduction for church contributions?"

Following Tom's advice, John turned in an income tax statement in which he claimed larger deductions than those he was
entitled to make.   But John didn't have Tom's very elastic
conscience.   His plagued him, and he became ill.   The illness

was psychosomatic.   So was the fatigue that accompanied it.

For individuals who have violated their own consciences, fatigue can be a method of punishing themselves.

Their consciences say: "You have been very wicked.   You don't deserve to feel well or energetic."   And the body always follows the commands of the inner mind.   *If your conscience demands that you punish yourself with fatigue, you will.*

The salesman whose sales went down because his guilt feelings exhausted him.   In a lecture in Los Angeles, Dr. Norman Vincent Peale told about a certain man who used to be a terrific salesman, but whose sales had gone way down.

Dr. Peale invited the man to come up to his room and talk to him.

"I can't," said the man.   "I have to be up and at 'em."

"Well, that's fine," said Dr. Peale.   "I'm glad you have so much drive.   But I'm sure God doesn't intend us to drive ourselves to death.   You seem somewhat upset, and I think I may be able to help you."

So the man, still very much on edge, went to see Dr. Peale. After a few moments, he burst out with the story of what was troubling him.

He'd gotten involved with a married woman, and the relationship was making him miserable.   He felt unhappy and guilty.   These guilt feelings made it impossible for him to sleep soundly, do his work well, or feel energetic.   Saying he had to be up and at 'em was just talk.   He knew he should be working hard and enthusiastically, but he couldn't, because his sense of guilt was destroying his energy.

"Why not get yourself out of this affair?" asked Dr. Peale.

"I'm afraid of hurting her feelings," said the man miserably.

Dr. Peale convinced him that he was doing more harm by hanging on to this affair, which was shattering to his self-esteem and conscience, than he would be doing by leveling with the woman.

To his surprise when he told her that he wanted to break off their relationship, she seemed pleased.   She herself had wanted to end it, but had postponed telling him so.

Having given up this rather sordid affair, the man is again a top producer for his company.

A normal conscience will warn you against actions that are repellent to it, and in that way often save you from future remorse.

If you disobey its warnings, it will nag you, until you try to make restitution for any harm you have done. Where there is no way of making restitution, it will urge you to change your way of life, and end the course of action it labels dishonorable.

2. Avoid an unreasonable conscience

Says Dr. Judd Marmor: "Excessive guilt feelings are apt to be the result of a tyrannical conscience."

It is possible to have a conscience that is so exacting that its owner cannot rest day or night because of his perfectionistic standards. I once knew a wonderful minister whom his whole congregation revered. But he was so imbued with the belief that he was a miserable sinner and was not living up to his ideals, that he rarely had a peaceful night.

How to avoid an over-tyrannical conscience. Says Dr. Judd Marmor: "The best way to help people avoid getting 'overburdened consciences' is to raise children with tolerance and understanding, and without setting perfectionistic or unrealistic moral goals for them."

For instance, a clinical psychologist cites the case of Johnny, a five-year-old, who comes home from school, and confesses that he stole a pen from a classmate. Naturally his mother tells him that it was wrong for him to take it, and that he must return it. But if she is wise, she will also add: "Johnny, what you did is wrong, but we all make mistakes. That's the way we learn. Just try not to make the same mistake twice. Nobody is perfect."

If Johnny feels that his mother still loves him in spite of his mistake, he will probably not nourish excessive guilt feelings; and he will also avoid petty thefts in the future.

Suppose that instead his mother harangues him on the subject of honesty, weeps and wails about the fact that she has

raised a son who turned out to be a thief, and says she wishes
he had never been born.

By shoving Johnny's self-esteem into the gutter, she may be
playing havoc with his future life.   Now he feels not only that
he has committed an unpardonable crime, but also that he is a
rejected outcast.

*Our inner consciences are often based to a large extent on
what the significant persons in our childhood have told us.*
First, they may tell us: "Don't do this.   Don't do that."   And
they may punish us if we go against their orders.   Later an
inner voice says to us: "Don't do that."   When we go contrary
to that inner order, we are apt to punish ourselves with physical
symptoms and with fatigue.

If we find that our inner voice is unrealistic in its demands,
we should stop demanding perfection of ourselves.

A young secretary new to the ways of the business world was
told by her boss that whenever a certain unwelcome caller
'phoned, she was to say that her employer was not in.   This
advice threw her into a terrific conflict.   Having been brought
up on perfectionistic standards, which included never telling
even the whitest of white lies, she was horrified by her boss's
instructions.   Following them made her miserable.   Her tor-
mented conscience interfered with her sleep and therefore
with her energy.

Finally, she confessed her problem to an unprejudiced outsider.   He said: "Your boss simply means that he is not in to
this unwelcome caller.   Don't you think it's better to say so
than to tell this caller that your boss doesn't want to talk to
him?   If your boss is always out to him, he'll catch on."

This explanation soothed the secretary's conscience, and she
was once again able to sleep nights.

3. Seek the help of religion

Worship a god of mercy and kindness, and do not bow your
knees to a god whose only purpose is punishment.

If you believe in such a god, you will always feel guilty and

lose energy as a result.   Believe in a god of love, and that belief will fill you with abundant energy.

The great religions of the world teach, "God is love."

We, who are said to be made in His image, can fulfill ourselves on earth mainly by practicing love.

Love of God, of our children, of our families, of our mates,
of our friends, gives us new energy, abundant and overflowing.
Hatred can grab that energy and exhaust it, and so can fear.
So why should we live lives wilted by fear and hate?

It is an insult to Almighty God to hate yourself, to refuse to
accept His divine image within yourself.   Somewhere within
yourself there is a voice that should tell you how you can live
your life so that God, who is all goodness, would approve of
your actions.

The stock salesman who became a great sales supervisor
through love of God and other human beings.   For instance,
Jim Terrell, director of sales training for the southern offices
of Paine, Webber, Jackson & Curtis, a famous investment firm,
admits there was a time in his life when he wasn't deeply religious.   At that time his feeling about most sales was: "What's
in it for me?"

When he first started out as a stock salesman, if a woman
ignorant of investments had come to him for advice, he might
have thought, "Why, this is just like taking candy from a baby."
Instead of asking himself, "What's in it for her?" he might have
advised stocks that would result in the biggest commissions
for himself.

Then he became interested in the study of metaphysics, and
began to realize that he had been created in God's image and
was expected to do God's will on earth, not just his own.

One day a widow, completely unversed in a knowledge of
investments, came to him for guidance.

He told her he would consider her problem thoughtfully.
Before choosing her investments, he prayed that he would be
guided to choose stocks that would be right for her.   There
were many speculations on which he could have made higher

commissions, but he chose blue chip investments that were just right for her particular circumstances.

In the years since then, the widow has prospered, and so has Jim. Because he feels that he is acting only in accordance with what he believes to be right, he has three times the enthusiasm and five times the energy he used to have in the days when he was acting purely in the interests of Jim Terrell and family.

He owes his important position, too, to the fact that he is interested in others. While still a stock salesman, he went out of his way to help younger salesmen who didn't know how to make frequent and successful sales. An older man watched Jim's helpful ways with other salesmen. And later on, when he learned of an opening as a director of sales training in a large investment firm, he recommended Jim for it.

Since then Jim has risen steadily in the investment business. He realizes that to have a full quota of energy, you must believe in what you are doing and act in the best interests of your customers. Sometimes, if he feels that a prospective customer should not be in the stock market at all, he tells him so. "I'm not afraid of losing a sale that way," he says. "The lost sale that was wrong for the customer will probably lead him to recommend you to someone else, who really should be in the market."

4. Avoid guilt feelings about your thoughts

Dr. Judd Marmor says: "It is expecting too much of people to expect them never to have thoughts that are unacceptable to their own consciences. Every human being at some time or other has such thoughts, but there is a tremendous difference between *having* a thought and *acting* on it."

We needn't have guilt feelings about the thoughts that try to get into our heads, as long as we reject them. Loeb and Leopold, to mention one famous example, would never have committed murder if they had rejected the thought the instant it came to them, instead of welcoming it into their minds.

Sometimes we have vague and unfocused feelings of guilt, because of thoughts we hesitate to admit even to ourselves.

If you suffer from chronic exhaustion and cannot determine its cause, you may be sapping your strength because all your energies are being absorbed by nameless guilt feelings.

HOW TO TELL WHETHER GUILT FEELINGS ARE THE CAUSE OF YOUR TIREDNESS

If you are suffering from overwhelming guilt feelings, how can you tell whether they are the cause of unnecessary fatigue?

There are two questions you can ask yourself that will help you determine this:

1. Do you sometimes feel as if you hate yourself?

If you find your own personality difficult to accept, the chances are that you are suffering from exaggerated guilt feelings.

2. Do you wake up feeling tired?

If you do, it may be an indication that several times at night you have been having emotional wrestling matches with your unconscious conscience.

Now dreams in themselves need not be harmful. It has been established by scientists that during the course of eight hours' sleep most of us dream for an hour and a half, at different times during the night. Sigmund Freud stated that far from being disturbers of sleep, most dreams are the guardians of our rest. In our dreams we can remake the world temporarily the way we'd like it to be. And if something happens that might disturb our sleep, like sudden flashes of light or sudden noises, our unconscious minds will often weave these things into the fabric of dreams, so we can go on slumbering.

However, there are certain nightmares that are disturbing to sleep and rest.

Naturally, most of us would like to avoid these.

According to psychiatrists, such dreams are mostly due to our own fears of our inner emotions. Within each of us are primitive instincts and desires, which for all we know may date back to the cavemen. When we repress these aggressive instincts completely and deny that they exist, they are turned inward. Then the aggressive instincts we have refused to admit we have, turn into the unconscious conscience, which can be so tyrannical.

Suppose a great army had gathered together, to fight the army of a foreign country. Then for some reason the war was called off. But the army's bloodthirsty instincts were still there, only now there was no external enemy to wage war on. How long do you think it would be before the men turned on each other?

When an ordinary individual tries to suppress all his native aggressiveness, those instincts swamp him. There is no longer any external victim; he is the victim. And the nightmares are the result of his fear of himself.

Nobody knows for sure whether we are born with destructive instincts, or whether they are the result of frustration. Actually, it doesn't matter. In either event, it would be ridiculous to overlook the fact that our energy comes from two sources: the urge toward aggression and the urge toward love.

Frequently individuals become alarmed because they recognize in themselves certain aggressive instincts. Now these have been given to us for some purpose. Without them, we might be lacking to a certain extent in drive. If we deny that we have them, we do so at our peril. If they sink into the unconscious mind, we will have anxiety dreams about the monster that rages within us.

We must learn to harness our aggressive trends. For instance, the Western representative of a certain magazine was steaming because he was given a run-around by the representative of one of the big publicity firms. Instead of continuing to smolder, he called the publicity man on the carpet, and asked why he was being stalled on his request for a certain interview.

The publicity man said, "But we're so busy we just didn't have time to take care of it."

The Western editor said, "I'd be ashamed to say that I was too busy to do my job. If your firm is too busy to handle all its accounts, why doesn't it drop a few?"

The result of this plain-speaking was that the Western editor got the interview he needed. He had been stern but fair. He had used his aggressive feelings to help the magazine for which he was working. He didn't really hurt anyone else.

If he had suppressed his aggression, he would have done a poorer job for the magazine.

Aggression and kindness can exist side by side. You can be aggressive against injustice, unkindness, unfairness wherever and whenever you find them. Dr. Schweitzer, one of the greatest men in the world today, uses his aggression against illness in the jungles of Africa.

If you are naturally aggressive, thank heaven for it. If you use your aggressiveness in your work, it will not disturb you in your sleep. You never hear of lumberjacks having anxiety dreams and waking up tired. Felling trees helps them get rid of their aggressiveness. And most of the important jobs in the world today demand a certain amount of aggressiveness. So discharge your aggression normally during the day. That doesn't mean getting into big fights about little things. You must use your aggressiveness in the service of other human beings, not in hurting them.

One of the greatest teachers who ever lived was showing aggression when He drove the money changers out of the temple. He didn't hate the money changers, but just what they were doing.

When to see a psychiatrist. If you consistently suffer from guilt feelings, and if they rob you of energy and interfere with a normal life, you should see a psychiatrist. Psychiatry is expensive, it is true, but what could be more expensive than to rob yourself of the ability to live and work like a normal human being?

Most of us hate to see ourselves drained of money, but our energy is the true source of our money-making power. If we are lacking in energy, we won't be able to earn as much money as when we are well-adjusted and at least reasonably happy.

How to relieve guilt feelings when psychiatry isn't necessary. Sometimes, even without psychiatric help, guilt feelings can be channeled into constructive activities.

Take, for instance, the moving story of Dean Hess. When the Japanese struck at Pearl Harbor, he was a Protestant minister in Marietta, Ohio. Later, he became a fighter pilot in the U. S. Air Force.

As a fighter pilot on combat missions over Germany and Korea, he often had to let loose the forces of destruction. When he discovered that he had accidentally bombed a building used by schoolchildren, he was filled with terrible guilt feelings, which preyed on his mind day and night.

He took his problem to God in prayer, and God opened the way for him to salve his feelings of guilt.

When he discovered that thousands of defenseless Korean orphans were endangered by the onsweeping Chinese Communist armies, he organized the airlift by which they were flown to safety. Then he established an orphanage to take care of them.

The energy he'd previously wasted on regrets and guilt feelings was transformed into a breath-taking new type of creative energy.

The secret behind the transformation of some men from Zombies into very effective individuals.   Col. Hess's story reveals the secret magic behind many transformations of unhappy, lethargic individuals into creative, happy ones. Our negative emotions exhaust us. Therefore, to release and conserve energy, we must transform negative emotions into positive ones. When we change guilt feelings into a pulsating desire to do good, new energy is released for our new purpose in life.

The man who had to lead two lives to keep from feeling exhausted.   When he was only 18, Dr. Donald Curtis, now minister of the Science of Mind Church of Religious Science in Los Angeles, California, accidentally ran over a young boy. The child had come racing out of an alley on his bicycle so suddenly that even the quick reflexes of 18-year-old Donald weren't swift enough to stop his big truck in time. The boy died as the result of the accident.

No one blamed Donald for what had happened, but day and night his tortured conscience cried out, "Because of you, a young boy is dead." He visited all sorts of churches seeking an answer through religion, but at this time no answer came to him.

At the child's funeral, the boy's father said to him, "I freely and fully forgive you for what happened. But you must remember that you must now lead two lives to make up for the one you unintentionally took. You must live not only for yourself but for my dead son, too."

The words penetrated deeply into young Donald's mind. But at first he didn't see how he could do anything to atone for the accident. He became an actor and played many roles on the stage, in pictures, and in radio. However, deep within him surged a feeling of discontent. At the end of each day he felt exhausted, with that exhaustion that comes when one's work is not the answer to one's deepest needs.

In spite of his success, a feeling of unresolved guilt haunted him most of the time. He remembered that the boy's father had said that he must lead two lives.

Was his work as an actor sufficient to atone for the child's death? In his heart, Donald didn't think so. What would the boy's life have been like if he had grown to manhood? Donald didn't know. Still seeking an answer, he began to study Science of Mind. There he found the answers he had been seeking ever since his truck had collided with a young boy's bicycle.

But it was not enough to find those solutions for himself. He felt a spiritual responsibility to bring them to others whom they might help. And so he decided to lead two lives. So long as it was necessary, he would support himself by acting, while he studied for the ministry. The ministry would be his second life.

When he made up his mind to do this, he was imbued with enough energy for two people.

He has transformed his guilt feeling, which formerly preyed

on his mind, into constructive energy.   Now he is dedicated to
helping others—and has energy to spare.

A worth-while purpose can double your energy.   About two
years ago, Dr. Curtis decided to give up his acting career, except when it offered unusual opportunities to accomplish good.
When he consciously channeled his double-barreled energy
into his work in the ministry, he felt a great surge of power.
This has enabled him to help others through sermons, individual consultations, classes, and radio talks.   All his energy is
now concentrated on his one big purpose in life—helping others.

Destructive energy can be transformed.   So if you suffer
from intense remorse for some mistake you have made, something that cannot be undone, atone by trying to do something
constructive in the world.   Just as in physics you cannot destroy matter or energy, you cannot actually destroy it in the
world of the spirit and mind.   But you can transform energy
that is being used destructively into energy that will accomplish something useful.

THE EFFECT OF SEX ON ENERGY

Probably one of the greatest causes of exaggerated guilt
feelings in our modern world is sex maladjustment.

Many individuals believe that sex in any form is a drain on
one's energy.   That isn't so.   Says Dr. Judd Marmor: "Contrary to popular belief, a satisfactory sex life increases one's
sense of energy rather than the other way around.   Usually
with an unsatisfactory sex life much energy is lost in internal
conflict and in feelings of frustration."

But what is a satisfactory sex life?   For most of us, a satisfactory sex life is intimately tied up with the emotion of love.
If a man is in love with one woman, and has an affair with
another, he will usually suffer from remorse.   On the other
hand, when sex is tied up with all one's devotion to another
human being, when love and its most intimate expression exist
side by side, we become infused with energy and enthusiasm.

HOW TO ACHIEVE A SATISFACTORY SEX LIFE

How can we achieve a satisfactory sex life and find the wonderful energy that comes from such a life?

1. Fresh thinking on what's normal in sex and what isn't

Psychiatrists tell us that thousands of young men and women suffer mental tortures that exhaust them physically and emotionally because of indulgence in habits that are exceedingly widespread.

Masturbation is a childish method of solving one's sex needs. Carried to excess, it is as bad as any other habit indulged in immoderately.

It does not, psychiatrists tell us, lead to insanity, epilepsy, or any dread disease. On the whole, worrying about it does more harm than the habit itself.

If it is indulged in moderately in childhood and adolescence, and abandoned for a more mature method of sex release later on, it does no great harm. Many men and women seek it at times for the relief of tensions; but it does not have the relaxing effect of a happy sex relationship.

As a rule, it is much more fatiguing than normal sex relationships. Often, the practice in men is accompanied by fantasies of beautiful women in order to make it more acceptable. But the fantasies vanish, increasing a man's sense of loneliness, his knowledge of the wide gap between fantasy and reality. As the dreams vanish, his fatigue increases.

However, indulgence in masturbation should not lead to excessive self-condemnation. In fact, some neurotic individuals, knowing how it causes their self-esteem to crumble, may even use it as a means of self-punishment, some authorities tell us. In such cases, it is almost always followed by extreme fatigue.

Since exaggerated guilt feelings about what is normal in sex cause so much fatigue and loss of energy, I asked Dr. Judd

Marmor: "If a patient asks, 'Doctor, what is normal in sex?' is there any particular book on the sex relationship to which you would refer him?"

Three helpful books on sex. Dr. Marmor replied: "A competent book on this subject is Dr. Van De Velde's, *Ideal Marriage* (New York: Random House, 1930). Another satisfactory book is Hannah and Abraham Stone's *Marriage Manual* (New York: Simon and Schuster, 1953). A third book that is quite satisfactory and relatively inexpensive is *Sex Manual* by G. Lombard Kelly, published by the Southern Medical Supply Company, Augusta, Georgia (available only through physicians)."

2. Sex energy can be sublimated

Can unused sex energy be sublimated and turned into useful, creative energy in other directions? I asked Dr. Judd Marmor this question. He said: "I believe that it is possible to achieve sublimation to a considerable extent at least, in artistic, creative, or altruistic work."

Dr. Sigmund Freud believed that the great artistic and scientific achievements of Leonardo da Vinci, the genius of the 15th and early 16th century, were partly due to sublimated sex energies.

Love, properly directed, makes our energies greater, not less. This is the great message of religion, philosophy, and psychology. Whether love is expressed sexually or through friendship, whether it is love for one's mate, one's neighbor, or one's God, love is the secret source of our greatest energy. This is not just theory; it is a scientific fact.

The experiment that proved the Sermon on the Mount works to produce more energy. At Harvard, a group of sociologists decided to test just how effective the Sermon on the Mount is in the treatment of modern problems of love and hate, and in the release of energy through love.

A group of five college students volunteered as subjects. Each of them disliked a different individual. Each promised to try to be kind, good, and friendly to the man or woman he disliked, thus carrying out the injunction, "Love thy enemies."

The final result of this strange experiment was that each man or woman learned to love the neighbor he had formerly despised, and as a result of that love was imbued with new energy and greater faith in God and man.

The conclusion of the eminent scientists was: "The Sermon on the Mount actually works!"

It does indeed.

And along with the Ten Commandments it offers the world's greatest prescription for avoiding unnecessary guilt feelings that sap our energy and destroy our love of life.

IN A NUTSHELL:
FOUR WAYS TO AVOID EXAGGERATED GUILT FEELINGS

1. Try to avoid doing things that your conscience warns you against.

2. Try to avoid having a tyrannical and unreasonable conscience.

3. Seek the help of religion, or the help of philosophy. Worship a god of mercy, love, and kindness, not a divinity whose only purpose is punishment and torment.

4. Don't feel guilty because you sometimes have thoughts that are against your moral principles. Don't welcome those thoughts, but don't condemn yourself for occasionally having them.

How to achieve a sex life that builds up energy instead of destroying it:

1. Don't accept the old-fashioned ideas of laymen on what is normal in sex and what isn't. Ask a psychiatrist, or study a good book on sex.

2. Don't go in for sex relationships that destroy your self-esteem, or hurt other individuals.

3. Let love, not hate, direct your energies in sex, and so far as possible, in other activities.

10

How to Control Your Energy
Storehouse to Promote
Peace of Mind

*I*F YOU FREQUENTLY FEEL EXHAUSTED OR JUST HAVEN'T ENOUGH energy to accomplish what you want to, there are two possible reasons for this.

Maybe, on the one hand, you don't build up strong enough impulses of love, tenderness, and enthusiasm to fill your mental energy tank to the brim. You put very little out; you get very little energy back. That's why Part 1 of this book was devoted to showing you how to build up the emotional storehouse of your energy.

However, it's possible that your emotional storage tank is filled to capacity. Still, except for sudden bursts of energy, you're exhausted most of the time. That's because you are storing and using the wrong emotions to give you drive, or are using them in the wrong way.

Everyone has an emotional storage battery of energy. Your energy depends largely on your emotions. The thoughts and actions you release flow outside of yourself into the world. There they usually awaken feelings very like yours—love when

152

you give out love, and hatred when you give out hate. Love returns multiplied many times to refill your energy tank. Hate, returning, also comes back multiplied by the hate it has created. In return, you respond to the emotions you have aroused with more hate or more love.

When you feel and act positively, your positive emotions, accompanied by the good will they generate, return to replenish the energy tank.

When you think hateful, negative, and destructive thoughts, energy starts to flow from the tank at a tremendous rate into the outside world; or else those feelings surge inside you, tearing you to pieces.

Negative emotions overcharge your batteries. Someone convinced you that John is a scoundrel. You begin to hate him, and to treat him with such suspicion and resentment that he senses it and in turn starts to dislike you intensely. Soon your worst fears about John come true. He tells all his friends what an untrustworthy so and so *you* are. The more John hates you, the more you hate him.

Initially this hatred you feel doesn't destroy your energy. Instead it builds the energy in your emotional storage tank almost up to the bursting point.

You're so tense you complain that your batteries are overcharged. Then the next thing you know you're weak as a kitten. Where did the mysterious burst of energy go?

It short-circuited.

Whenever you are filled with destructive emotions, they may give you a lot of immediate physical energy, but in the end they will go out into the world and destroy others, or turn back on you to destroy you. No matter how great the immediate burst of energy you get in this way, the final result is death to energy power, plus frequent physical and mental symptoms of illness.

You may believe that you cannot control your emotions. However, you can change your way of looking at things; you can actually change your feelings. And when you change your feelings, you *control* the effect they have on you.

For instance, if you are unduly sensitive, you can learn to recognize the fact that when Joe Blow criticizes you, it is often because he is upset about something in his own personal life. When you are more self-confident, you will be tolerant toward Joe Blow, rather than over-concerned about his unfair criticisms. You will learn to benefit by criticism when the critic knows what he is talking about, and to shed your anxiety rapidly in the case of those who criticize for the sake of criticizing. Having gotten rid of morbid over-sensitivity, you will be able to avoid its upsetting effects. You'll no longer feel that your whole day is ruined by an unkind remark, and you won't get unduly angry at Joe Blow.

Besides controlling the *effects* of your negative emotions, you can *channel* the emotions themselves so that they bring you peace of mind instead of destruction.

First of all, you must not fear your destructive emotions. They were given to you, just as the power to love was given to you, to be used for good purposes.

Neither fear nor hate nor anger is in itself vicious. They become vicious only when they are used destructively, or when they inspire you to withdraw from normal social contacts.

You must not be afraid of your own aggressiveness. You were born to be aggressive.

You were not born to be a Caspar Milquetoast, sitting on your derrière, worrying and brooding about what others will think of you. You were not born to fight this aggression within you and to whip yourself mentally because all your thoughts are not pure, sweet, and kind.

You were born to hate as well as to love. It is *what* you hate and what you *do* about it that counts.

Dr. Howard Bierman hated cancer for its destructiveness of human life. He hated the negative attitude that most medical men took toward leukemia. They believed that the illness was not only destructive and fatal, but that there was nothing that could be done about it.

He gave up a good medical practice to devote himself to the enemy he hated—leukemia. He hated seeing what it did to adults, to helpless children. But he used his hatred of leukemia to study the illness, to revolutionize the world concept of it from absolute helplessness to an attitude of hope.

He found that leukemia offered a chance to study the origins and changing forms of cancer. If a woman was stricken with cancer of the breast, you couldn't perform a biopsy every hour —no woman would stand for that—but changes in blood cells, such as occur in leukemia, could be studied hourly by the simple process of pricking the skin with a needle for a blood test.

There was a time when a man with leukemia might say, "How many months have I to live?" Today, the older you are when you get leukemia, the more hopeful the outlook is. And some day leukemia and possibly all cancers may be vanquished, all because there are men like Dr. Bierman, who is scientific director of the City of Hope Medical Center. Such men have used their hatred and their aggressiveness to fight against one of mankind's oldest enemies.

We can't all be Dr. Biermans, and fight against cancer. But there are slums that should be eliminated, poor traffic laws that should be changed, corrupt city machines that can be uprooted from politics, mental hospitals that aren't run properly. There are old people's homes that are a national disgrace. When a newspaperman or any other individual crusades against one of these things, and succeeds in improving the situation just a little for the better, he has used his aggressiveness to good purpose.

Even anger can sometimes be channeled into fighting power. For instance, Oklahoma football guard Bill Krisher, according to an AP dispatch, gets very angry when an opposing player uses foul language. So what does he do about it? According to Bill Krisher, "I smile, say a little prayer for the guy, and hit him harder.

"I never try to hurt an opponent. I never have trouble holding my composure. But I put a little extra effort behind hitting an opponent when he uses foul language. Such language doesn't belong on the football field."

And so Bill Krisher turns his mild hate against foul language into fighting power and energy.

Anger, aggressiveness, hate—we've been taught to be afraid of these emotions. And it's easy to understand why. They can lead to physical violence.

But the emotions are not bad in themselves. Would you give two cents for a man who saw a child being violently abused and beaten, and didn't get angry? Would you give two cents for a soldier who never had the good sense to know when to be afraid? And what is a man worth who doesn't have enough aggressiveness to fight for anything? Even Gandhi's non-violent resistance was a form of fighting.

If you want to control your emotional storage tank, remember this first of all:

1. Do not be afraid of negative emotions

Learn to turn them to positive uses. If you are ashamed of your normal hatreds, you might try to suppress them completely, and this is dangerous.

When you hate but dare not admit it even to yourself, your bottled up hatred may make you physically ill.

This hatred can give you a drive that may make you a success in your work for a little while. But if you get your drive and your energy this way, beware! Energy derived from personal hatred is rapidly exhausted. So is energy derived from fear.

Very often fear creates hatred. A young man who had been a brilliant mechanical engineer became frightened when another man, equally brilliant, started to work alongside him in his firm. Actually, the concern could use both men.

But John, the first employee, instead of regarding the situation as an interesting challenge, considered it a frightening threat. Because of his fears, he tensed up physically. Because he tensed up physically he began to suffer from rigid neck muscles, moist palms, and a pain in the back of his neck.

His tension built up more fears. His job, he feared, wasn't safe. He was afraid of impending disaster.

Years passed, and he didn't lose his job, but he dropped all his hobbies, for fear that if he kept them up, he wouldn't be able to keep up with the competition in his own firm.

He began to isolate himself from other men, even those in his company. When the time came to promote one of the two engineers, the one who had been hired more recently got the promotion. Actually because he was not afraid, he had more energy. He had enough vitality to go out and make friends, as well as to be a good mechanical engineer.

Eventually John went to see a psychiatrist. The psychiatrist said, "The situation has not made you tense. Rather it is your *reaction* to it that accounts for your tenseness. All your life, you have been over-reacting. Now you must learn to react normally."

This particular psychiatrist believes that if we can become less tense physically, many of our emotional ills will disappear. He told John, "You need some training in physical relaxation. Have you noticed that you are subject to the symptoms you complain of only when you are tense? With increasing skill in relaxation, you will be able to get rid of these symptoms."

For 15 minutes a day, John practiced complete physical relaxation, starting by learning to relax the large muscles in his legs and arms, and later the smaller ones. He learned, too, to relax his formerly rigid neck muscles.

Now some psychiatrists may feel that this is a pretty superficial way of attacking the problem. But it worked! It was combined with a certain amount of psychiatry. However, instead of giving the usual 50 minute hour to his patient, this particular psychiatrist, a fine professor of psychiatry at a great university, saw him for 15 minutes a day.

John learned to be competitive with himself, instead of with the other members of the firm. Relaxed physically and emotionally, he could attack his problems with gusto instead of fear.

"You have been a perfectionist all your life," the psychiatrist told John. "But perfection is something we cannot achieve on earth. It is a goal, and cannot be turned into a concrete achievement."

reaved one seems to find no constructive outlet for his energy, a visit to a psychiatrist is called for.

2. When your problems seem too much for you . . .

Whenever anything seems too much to take, remember that "this, too, will pass."

Sidney Epstein, owner of the Shine-Phillips Company of Los Angeles, which specializes in moving movie props from one location to another, was a captain in Tunisia during World War II.

This philosophy, that everything passes, helped him tremendously during the war when three tanks were shot from under him. Each time part of his crew was killed.

"I had to preserve enough peace of mind to help save the men who were left. I shut off my emotions as best I could.

"If an officer suffered every time one of his men was killed, he would end up with battle fatigue. Then what use would he be to his men?

"So during the War, I taught myself to think, 'Everything passes.' No matter how tough something may be, it will be over in 10 minutes, half an hour, an hour, or whatever length of time is required.

"When you are confronted with a difficult or tragic situation, you can waste your energy by fighting mentally against it, or you can acquire the knack of adapting to it. Actually, we haven't the strength to fight both ourselves and the situation, so we must learn to concentrate on fighting only the problem.

"Some men, from the minute they first got into the Army, didn't like other soldiers, didn't like the food, didn't like anything about Army life. Now no one in his right mind would pretend that war is anything but what Sherman called it— hell—but in such a situation, you are much better off if you can learn to make the best of it and stop grumbling about something over which you have no control.

"When you cannot change a situation, you have to accept it. And acceptance is usually eased if you remember that the thing you are fighting against or despairing about will eventually pass."

Because he trained himself to shut off his emotions of horror during the war, it's very simple for Sidney Epstein to face the ordinary headaches of business without becoming unduly disturbed by them.

He says, "I don't look for trouble, but can handle it if it arises. I can work 12 hours a day without becoming fatigued because my work interests me, and I don't let my emotions get in the way. I know that everything passes—and that includes both big and little troubles."

The knowledge that everything passes and that eventually some good may come out of happenings that seem terrible at the time of their occurrence will release a great flood of energy in you. This is the energy that is normally wasted by asking, "Why did this have to happen?" and in *rebelling* against the fact that it *did* happen.

Instead, accept what has happened as unchangeable. Ask yourself: "What lesson can I learn from this experience? What good can I accomplish with what I have learned from it?" Finding the answers to these questions will enable us to turn the dross of the most unfortunate experience into the gold of purpose and energy.

3. Expend energy creatively, not destructively

Some psychiatrists (following the lead of Sigmund Freud) tell us that there are two deep instincts in us: the life instinct, which seeks to build up glorious life in us; and the death instinct, whose purpose it is to lead us to our final end.

The death instinct doesn't always lead directly to suicide or to death through illness. There are more ways than one of dying, and some of them are quite subtle. Sometimes instead of living fully, we cunningly destroy our energy through the will to fail. This will to fail, which is opposed to the wish to live an abundant life, may lead us to seek all kinds of destructive ways to misuse our energy.

The compulsive gambler, the compulsive drinker, the com-

pulsive eater—all are victims of the will to fail. The obese
man whose doctor has warned him that he had better shed
some fat if he wants energy and long life but who cannot discipline himself is just as much a victim of the will to fail as the
man who becomes a slave to narcotics.

Andrew was a compulsive eater. When he was a youngster,
his mother over-emphasized the importance of his favorite
foods. It was not extraordinary for him to have two steaks, a
plate of spaghetti, and a few sausages for breakfast, often lovingly served to him while he lolled in bed.

To Andrew, food became the great comforter, a refuge in
times of trouble. If someone annoyed him or he was faced
with any frustration, he ate his favorite foods in huge quantities.

When things went smoothly, however, he was a charming,
friendly individual, expert at dealing with people. So great
were his talents along this line that he became a successful
salesman, and eventually a sales manager.

He might easily have risen to become vice-president in
charge of sales of his company, for his executive ability was
unusual. But he found it hard to accept opposition from other
men in the organization. When his superiors disagreed with
his policies, he would fall into a silent rage. To pacify himself, he went back to the "comfort foods" of his childhood.

Whenever he was faced with a challenge, he regarded it as
a frustration. He would then begin feeling sorry for himself.
And whenever he was sorry for himself, he overate.

His obesity cut into his energy. It was a vicious circle.
When things went wrong he overate; and when he overate, he
felt sluggish, and didn't bring the same brainpower to his problems as previously. So more things went wrong.

Every once in a while he would go on a diet. But as soon
as he lost a few pounds, he would go off it; then gain those
pounds back. With each gain in weight, he would find himself getting more and more easily fatigued.

His doctor had warned him that his habit of overeating was
cutting into his vitality. But his gluttony seemed greater than

his desire for energy and success. With less energy, he accomplished less, was less inspiring to his salesmen and to potential customers. He was in danger of losing his job.

It is harder to cure obesity than cancer. Dr. Donald Petit of the University of Southern California recently stated that the percentage of cures in obesity cases is much smaller than in cancer.

Why? Because over-indulgence in food goes back, in many cases, to childish habits and ideas. When we were children, our parents often gave us rich foods and desserts to console us when we were unhappy, or to reward us for good behavior. As adults, when we yield to self-pity, overeating seems a natural way to comfort ourselves.

Andrew's will to fail could be changed into a will to succeed by directing his energy toward conquering self-pity instead of yielding to it. However, Andrew doesn't seriously want to remain successful. He wills himself to be self-indulgent, and he is. His energy is being spent on self-pity, resentment, hostility toward others, and gluttony.

The reserves of energy we all have are waiting to be used, or, if we prefer it that way, to be misused.

There are many ways to misuse that energy. It is possible to misuse it by going on a constant round of parties, doing no productive work at all. If you stay up till the wee hours five nights a week, you may have little energy left for anything but party-going. Why be so surprised that you are fatigued? Being on a perpetual merry-go-round takes energy, too.

Another way of destroying your energy is to talk about your ideas instead of putting them into action. Your energy can be frittered away talking about future accomplishments.

Shut up and get going! Forgive me for this plain talk. But the river that is dammed up is the one that eventually releases the most power.

If, every time you get a good creative idea, you talk about it, someone else will probably carry it to fulfillment. I remember once interrupting a novelist who was in the middle of telling my husband, myself, and a group of other people at our table, the plot of the novel he was going to write. "If you continue to talk about your novel," I warned, "you may never write it."

"You mean because someone else will beat me to it? I'll have it copyrighted."

"I didn't mean that, exactly. If you use up your drive to write discussing what you are going to write, you won't have enough energy to do the actual work."

Watch out for destructive uses of energy. They run the gamut from talking in too much detail about what we plan to do, to letting the sands of our energy run out in too much party-going.

Even too much concentration on work, with no rest and no vacations, can be destructive. If you want to remain normally healthy in mind and body, you won't go to extremes in anything—not even in work.

4. Ask yourself why you feel the emotions you do

Too much self-analysis is probably dangerous. But if you find yourself constantly flying off the handle or getting peevish with slight cause, it's time to ask yourself why.

Ralph, the son of a successful lawyer, married a charming woman. Soon, however, their married life became a series of constant bickerings. Everything his wife did and said seemed to irritate him. His constant irritability wore down his energy; both his law practice and his marriage suffered.

Finally, when Ralph and his wife were near the breaking point, he agreed to see a marriage counselor.

The counselor discovered that though Ralph loathed law, he had entered it at his father's insistence. He had a much greater interest in art, but not enough faith in himself to follow it up.

The counselor encouraged him to take up art as a hobby.

The basic cause of his marital bickerings had been his belief that his wife expected him to become as big a success in law as his father.

Actually, this was not important to her. When he dis-

covered that he had misinterpreted her feelings, he ceased to
feel the resentment that had caused him to pick on her.
Though his wife encouraged him to study art if he wished to
do so, he decided, for practical reasons, to continue with his
law practice. He no longer felt that he had to be better at his
career than his father. It had been the compulsion to compete with his father, mixed with a belief that he wasn't really
capable of competing successfully, that had drained his energy.
His conflict had caused him to resent both his father and his
wife. Once he realized the true reason for his resentments,
he was able to overcome them.

*Resentments, especially repressed resentments, rob you of
energy.* Whenever you find yourself resenting someone, try
to figure out why you resent them; then remove the cause of
your resentment, if possible. Often the cause is in *you*, not in
them. Don't assume that you know what *their* emotions are.
If you are bitter about a situation, try to compose yourself, to
see it objectively; then clear the air if you feel you have an
honest grievance. Often the best way to clear it is to have a
candid, unexcited discussion about the matter.

5. Conditioning your emotions

Teach yourself to feel the emotions you think you ought to
feel.

"What," you may say, "distort my emotions; twist and change
them? How can I do all that and still be myself?"

Actually, I'm not talking about distorting emotions, nor
about pretending to others that you feel emotions you really
don't have.

But if you are a shy, reserved person, you can *learn* to feel
happy and warm at the prospect of meeting someone new. If
you fear meeting others, you can waste a lot of energy on that
fear. If you are a person of many dislikes and few likes, you
can learn to look for the good in others, and stop concentrating
on your dislikes.

Two men went to a party. One said, "I hate this kind of
shindig, but I have to go in order to make certain business con-

tacts.   However, whenever such a contact is important to me,
I usually put my foot in it.   Whatever I say seems to be the
wrong thing."

The second man said, "What a wonderful opportunity to
meet new acquaintances.   I'm sure I'll make friends there."

The first man didn't enjoy one moment of the party.   He
met a man who might have become a valued client of his advertising firm, but because he expected to make a blunder, he
made one.

The second man had a wonderful time, and met several men
who have since become important in his life.   He was not
deliberately seeking a business contact; but he and a man he
met there liked each other, were favorably impressed with
each other's business acumen, and eventually entered into a
contract.

What we expect tends to influence what finally happens.
If, wherever you go, you carry your own built-in sense of liking
for others, you'll make friends everywhere.   If, on the other
hand, you've learned to dislike most individuals, you'll carry
that kind of feeling with you and have an unpleasant time
everywhere.

The choice is easy.   It is up to you.

You can be cheerful or gloomy.   If you want to sparkle
with energy, cut gloom as much as possible out of your emotional diet.   Look for things to be cheerful about.

It's the way you take everyday happenings that determines
whether you are filled with energy or easily exhausted.   Psychiatrists tell us that if we are gloomy, we have only a minimum amount of energy.

We are cyclic human beings, with plenty of ups and downs
in our moods, so there will be times when we are not feeling
100 per cent happy.

If we manage a cheerful smile even on those days, we'll soon
be feeling optimistic again.

6. Discuss your problems

Have calm and reasonable discussions with your family
about problems that disturb you.

Trying to suppress all discussions doesn't save energy, and doesn't properly control your energy storehouse. After all, the amount of energy available from the storehouse depends partly on your subconscious emotions. If you suppress all your resentments, they'll boil up inside of you. Every time you suppress an emotion and it finds its way into the subconscious, with it goes all the energy associated with it. That emotional energy may make it difficult for you to sleep; it may nag at you in nightmares.

The energy associated with an unpleasant suppressed emotion can be even more destructive than the original feeling.

Don't suppress your resentments. So you have moments when you hate your brother or sister, your mother, father, husband, or wife. That's quite normal. The psychologists have a two dollar word for it—ambivalence. It means that every emotion has two sides, that those we love most have the power at times to inspire temporary hatred in us.

If you resent something your brother or sister or anyone close to you has done, try to consider his point of view. How would you feel in his place?

Then have a quiet conference with him or her, and air your grievances. Dr. William Menninger and other authorities have said that we could overcome 50 per cent of the tiredness caused by emotional disturbances, if families would get together for calm and prompt discussions of problems tearing at them.

If you have a grievance against one member of your family, don't bring the others into it immediately. Try to settle it first between the two of you. By keeping relationships in your family harmonious, you can help build inner peace in yourself. Then, using your energy at an even, almost rhythmic rate, you can accomplish everything you've ever dreamed of.

Don't let your energy use you. When you are excited or filled with fears and hates, your energy may rise to a boiling point; it may become almost manic in character. In the end you won't be using it; it'll be using you to destroy you. Who in his right mind wants such destruction?

If you will work with others to destroy unpleasant things

that menace the community, then hate and fear cease to be dangerous. If you can hate the crime more than the criminal, greed more than the greedy, and even cruelty more than the sadist, you'll be able to help others as well as yourself.

How to be unselfishly selfish. A certain amount of selfishness is natural and seemingly instinctive. However, there have to be limitations on one's natural selfishness. Though selfishness and even ruthlessness may lead to temporary success, they never bring peace of mind. And without peace of mind, our mental health is always in danger.

In *The Stress of Life* (New York, Toronto, London: McGraw-Hill Book Company, Inc., 1956) Dr. Hans Selye, the noted scientist, says that we can solve the problem of how to be unselfishly selfish by living in such a manner as to inspire gratitude in others.

"I think in the final analysis," he writes, "that *gratitude and revenge are the most important factors governing our actions in everyday life;* upon them also depend our peace of mind, our feelings of security or insecurity, of fulfillment or frustration—in short, the extent to which we can make a success of life."

The more we inspire gratitude (the wish by others that we should prosper) the less stress we'll feel, he says. Also the less we inspire a desire for revenge in others, the better we'll feel. When we know that we have inspired hatred in others, we waste a lot of energy trying to convince ourselves that they have *no right* to hate us.

So let's try to earn good will. It's easy to knock on someone's door when you're trying to get your neighbor a job, but much harder when you wish to do something selfish for yourself. Knock on that door or make the phone call that will help someone you know. It'll make you feel better.

Don't do it because you expect to get anything but peace of mind out of it. But some day, when you least expect it, a door may be opened to you, because you once knocked on another door to help someone else.

SIX WAYS TO CONTROL YOUR ENERGY STOREHOUSE

1. Learn to direct your negative emotions into positive channels.

2. Whenever anything seems too much to take, remember that "This, too, will pass."

3. Expend energy constructively, not destructively; generously, but not wastefully.

4. Ask yourself why you feel the emotions you do.

5. Teach yourself to feel the emotions you think you ought to feel: cheerfulness instead of gloom; friendliness instead of shyness; a willingness to like others instead of an eagerness to look for faults.

6. When you are disturbed by something someone close to you has said or done, have a calm and reasonable discussion with him about it.

11

How to Use Your Energy to Achieve Your Goals

W OULD IT SURPRISE YOU TO LEARN THAT PSYCHOLOGISTS HAVE
now come to the conclusion that there is no such person as a
man without a goal?

Our lives portray our goals more loudly than we can name
them in words. Every bit of our behavior, every drop of our
energy is directed toward some goal.

Sometimes our energy is directed toward destructive goals.
There is the ne'er-do-well who goes on frequent benders, until
he is able to do nothing else. There is the town bum who
ends up on Skid Row after a series of unimportant jobs. There
is the man whose temperamental tantrums are such that he
can never hold a job for any length of time.

On the surface, all of these appear to be men without any
purpose in life. Actually, however, their unconscious goal is
failure.

It's a strange paradox that the unconscious mind—the greatest genie of the lamp ever discovered by man, the most wonderful servant, capable of fetching for us the greatest pearls
of wisdom—can, when it becomes our master, direct us head-
long into destruction.

When our energy is at the command of our unconscious minds, we can sometimes get into great trouble.

It takes just as much energy—sometimes more—to achieve willful failure as it does to achieve success, mental health, and a reasonable amount of happiness. But when our unconscious dictates our goals, that may be the way in which it directs our energies.

It takes energy to destroy your life. It takes as much energy to go insane as to stay mentally healthy.

It takes as much energy to destroy oneself with drink as to develop one's potential powers.

The successful criminal has as much energy as the saint. But he uses his energy differently. If he applied the same drive to achieving a worth-while goal, he could be a leader in his community.

Criminals aren't the only ones who use their energy to follow goals that ruin their lives and the lives of others.

Average individuals, pursuing neurotic goals they are not aware of, frequently use their energy to destroy themselves.

Let's take the case of Frank, a brilliant salesman. His boss decided that Frank might make an excellent sales manager.

Actually, Frank dreaded the leadership that was thrust upon him. But instead of frankly telling his boss about his feelings, he accepted the job.

From that time on, he was miserable. Because his natural talent was for selling, he felt like going out into the field and making all the sales himself. However, he knew that if he did his salesmen would resent it. He didn't really wish to teach his brilliant but unorthodox methods to his salesmen.

Since he avoided calling on customers in order not to antagonize his salesmen, he didn't have enough constructive outlets for his energy. To get his mind off his problems, he began to spend more and more time getting together with cronies for poker games, at which he proposed higher and higher stakes.

Soon his friends began to dread these games, for the stakes were so high that if they lost, their wives were furious. They found excuses to get out of playing with Frank. If they played, their wives also complained at being left alone night after night. Frank had gotten to the point where, instead of playing a sociable game once every week or two, he wanted to play poker every night.

He remembered that some forty miles away from the western city where he lived, there was a town where poker was legal, and was conducted in attractive gambling palaces.

First he began going to that town week-ends; then every day. In order to make the long drive each day, he left work earlier than ever before.

Gambling took the greater part of his energies. He had less and less time and energy to devote to sales management. Eventually he was fired.

On the surface, it looks as if Frank's goal was to get something for nothing. Gambling seemingly offered an opportunity to make money without having to work hard for it.

Actually, psychiatrists tell us that the goal of the gambler is rarely getting something for nothing. His real purpose is unconscious. Knowing that the odds are against him in any gambling palace, he unconsciously wants to lose. This is a form of self-punishment. Frank unconsciously wanted to punish himself because he was ashamed of his real attitude as a sales manager. He wanted his men to fail, because he was basically competitive rather than eager to help others. He didn't want anyone to equal his former sales record.

The gambler who devotes most of his energy to gambling can rarely be cured without psychiatric help.

Everyone has a goal, but not everyone knows what his goal is. That is why the thousands of professional psychiatrists we have are not really enough to service the United States. Other countries are, of course, no better off.

Hundreds of thousands of individuals are using their energy to destroy everything they say they want. They need to do an about-face. They must make their goals conscious, instead of keeping them completely under the dictation of the unconscious mind, or else their style of life will always lead to disaster.

Our actions speak loudly of our unconscious goals. You are fortunate if you have turned your unconscious mind into a willing slave. Then you can achieve almost anything on which you have set your heart.

But suppose, on the other hand, your energies are at the command of your unconscious mind—and you are *its* slave. Sigmund Freud once said that the individual is sometimes like a horseman who thinks he is riding a spirited horse, when in reality he is simply going where the horse wishes to take him. If your unconscious mind is directing you, and you live in obedience to impulses you do not understand, you are that helpless horseman.

How to discover your hidden goals

So you are faced with the problem: What kind of unconscious purpose is guiding your use of energy?

To find out, make a simple inventory of your life to date.

1. Who are you? What are you? Do you think of yourself primarily as a builder, a carpenter, a minister, a doctor, a skilled workman? What are your assets vocationally? Your liabilities?

2. What sort of a life do you have as a person? If you were in serious difficulties, to whom could you turn? Are you lonely and friendless, or do you have many friends?

3. What is the state of your mental health? Do you meet problems as quickly as possible, or procrastinate? Do you direct your energies toward a useful goal? What is it? How far have you gone toward achieving it?

4. Do you love or hate yourself? Do you wish you were anybody in the world except yourself? If your conscious goal is in harmony with your unconscious goal, you won't be smug, but you will accept yourself and you definitely will not be filled with self-hatred.

5. Is your life full of pressure? If it is, why have you allowed so many pressures to get the better of you? Don't you know when or how to say no?

6. Do you like to work?   Do you like the particular type of work you are doing?

7. What have you achieved materially?   A home of your own?   Savings toward such a home?   Money in the bank? Money in investments, preferably blue chips?   Or a morass of debts, and a series of speculations that went sour?

What you have today—spiritually, emotionally, intellectually, and financially—is the measure of your real goals.   Everything you have, everything you are tells exactly how you have so far directed your energies.

Some individuals believe that we are at the mercy of fate. But Dr. Sigmund Freud proved that to a large extent we create our own fate by the way we direct our energies.

Let's take three men, all of whom have great curiosity as one of their drives.   One man becomes the town gossip.   He has directed his energies toward a rather useless goal.   The second directs his drive into intellectual curiosity, and becomes a fine scholar.   The third becomes a scientist, and discovers a new wonder drug.

All three men started with the same drive, but each channeled his energies in accordance with his own goal.

Our biggest problem in achieving a goal is the habit of kidding ourselves as to what our goals really are.   If a man says he wants to be a good father but rarely spends any time with his son, some other aim is obviously much more important to him.   If a man says he wants to write, but spends all his spare time golfing, a career as a writer is obviously not important to him.

We always can find the time and energy for the things we really want.   If you never seem to have enough energy to achieve your conscious goals, most likely it is because your unconscious mind has other aims for you.   When your unconscious and conscious goals are at cross purposes, you become exhausted easily.   To use your energies wisely, you must bring your conscious and unconscious goals into harmony.

EIGHT STEPS TOWARD DIRECTING YOUR ENERGIES TO YOUR GOALS

1. Analyze yourself to find out your greatest drives

To get your unconscious as well as your conscious mind to back your goal, ask yourself what your serious interests in life really are. What are your greatest drives? At what do you spend the most time? Keep a chart of the way in which you spend a week's time. Analyze the number of hours you've spent at different tasks. Anything at which you spend an inordinate amount of time is a device for achieving a real goal.

Dr. Freud's great goal was to understand men's hidden motivations. Albert Schweitzer's goal, from the age of 30 on, has been to devote his energies to the natives in Africa. His friends told him that his goal was preposterous, that he was like a general who wishes to go out into the firing line with a rifle. "Why don't you lecture instead, to inspire others to go out and help those natives?" one friend suggested.

But Dr. Schweitzer knew exactly what he wanted to do. He has lived his life exactly as he planned it.

Very few of us can be Dr. Freuds or Dr. Schweitzers. Yet like the juggler, who with his humble juggling act pleased the Virgin he worshipped, each of us can please the supreme judge within himself by learning to do well something he is fitted for.

We must *want* to be something we *can* be. Wanting is the first step.

Intimations that come from our unconscious minds as to what we *want* are not necessarily blind urges. When the unconscious has a destructive purpose, it often hides that aim from our conscious minds. When the unconscious permits a drive to become conscious, the drive is usually something we can believe in and can be proud of. Such a goal has to be acceptable to a rational mind. The unacceptable drives can ordinarily be discovered only by a professional psychiatrist or through our actual behavior.

If your unconscious speaks, listen to it. The voice of the inner mind can be found in dreams, in reveries, in inspirations, and in sudden intuitions. These tell us how our energies should be directed.

When Dr. Havelock Ellis, the famous writer on sex problems, was a young man, he didn't know what vocation he wanted to follow. He thought of entering the church, and did some preaching in Australia. Not completely satisfied with this choice, he decided that he might try legal work.

One day, weary from work, he lay on a hard bench in a schoolroom, reading *The Life and Letters of James Hinton.* He liked to read in a horizontal position, for his mind seemed to function best under those circumstances.

When he read that a family doctor had influenced James Hinton by advising him to enter the medical profession, he jumped to his feet as though propelled by a cannon.

Instantly he knew, with almost magical certainty, that he wanted to become a doctor. The knowledge was so complete, so revelatory in character, that he never doubted it for a moment. His inner mind was speaking, and he listened. Later he realized that his unconscious had selected the medical profession because it offered the best approach to the kind of career that was really right for him—the writing of books about sex.

If Havelock Ellis had not become a doctor, it's very doubtful that his later views on sex, as expounded in his books, would have been received as authoritative. He had to know the anatomy of the human body and had to have a doctor's training in order to prepare for the career his unconscious mind had selected for him.

From somewhere deep within ourselves come these sudden urgings, nudging us in the right direction. And they are most likely to come to us when we are in a dream-like state, half between sleeping and waking.

Listen to these whispers that come from somewhere deep within yourself. Your unconscious may be telling you just how it wishes you to direct your energies.

You can't afford to ignore that voice deep within you. If your unconscious has selected a drive for you, it will make available to you a tremendous amount of energy to help you achieve that goal.

Later, we'll discuss how you can find out for yourself whether you have the abilities needed to achieve that goal. But your first step is to discover what your deep-seated drives are. Every unconscious drive carries with it a tremendous reservoir of energy.

2. Build up your desire for your goal

Really want it. Crave it. Think about it. Write it down. Name your important goals to yourself, then write them down. Write down each vital goal on a separate three by five card. When you go to bed at night, tuck one of these cards in a drawer of your night table. Before you fall asleep, say to yourself, "I am going to take every step necessary toward achieving this goal." Picture yourself achieving this goal. Then assign to your unconscious the task of figuring out the best steps to take.

If your goal is material, cut out a picture of it from a magazine or newspaper, or draw a picture of it, and paste it in a scrapbook, or on a bulletin board in your home. Look at that picture every morning when you wake up, and every evening before you go to sleep.

If you can convince your unconscious mind that you really crave something, it will become your ally. It will work while you sleep, as Robert Louis Stevenson's "Brownies" did in furnishing him inspiration for some of his best stories during his dreams.

Do you want the aid of the unconscious?

You cannot consciously control the hormones that regulate energy. But your unconscious mind can. If you need an even flow of energy, it will give it to you, provided you convince it through autosuggestion that there is something you really want to accomplish, for which you need that energy.

Dr. Freud labeled the deepest part of the unconscious "the

id." The "id" is sheer, primitive, demanding energy. It has no language but the cry, "I want."

You must do what it wants, or else convince it that there is something you want and must have from it. The "id" has immeasurable energy. Sometimes, however, it guards that energy like a dragon, releasing it only for its own purposes, or for goals that you have convinced it are its aims, too. You can do this by constant repetition and suggestion, particularly at night, just before you drop off to sleep.

So great is the influence of the unconscious on the direction of our energies that at a certain prison camp, Tulare County's Woodlake Road camp in California, Public Defender John Locke is trying the strange experiment of broadcasting tape-recorded messages through earphones near each convict's pillow.

According to a UP dispatch, a low voice whispers to each prisoner: "Listen, my inner self. Remember and obey the creed of life. Love, rule my life . . . forget the past . . . plan for the future and the future will take care of itself."

"The experiment," said Locke, "seeks to integrate, not disintegrate, the personality and to inculcate that love and not hate is the right way to live."

It will take four or five years to determine whether the goals of anti-social men can be changed by this pillow therapy. It is Mr. Locke's hope that the unconscious minds of his prisoners can be re-educated, so that they will direct their energies toward social goals.

If you are not achieving your goals, perhaps you, too, have been directing unconscious energies elsewhere. Of course, it's highly unlikely that your energies have been directed toward criminal purposes. But if you are wasting your boundless abilities on a thousand time-consuming and relatively useless activities, why not choose a worth-while goal? Then direct your energies toward that goal.

3. Pray for guidance, if you believe in prayer

Robert LeTourneau, who built a tremendous business devoted largely to earth-moving machines, says that we should not attempt to use God, but prayerfully ask God to use us.   He believes that when we try to do God's work, wonderful energies become available to us.   We are then using the greatest source of power known to humanity.

Once, when he was in great financial difficulties, he and his accountant were discussing the bills he owed.   He told his accountant that he wanted to dribble a small amount of money, if possible, to each creditor, as evidence of his good will and intention to pay.

Then the accountant came to Mr. LeTourneau's missionary pledge.   "Of course," said the accountant, "you can't pay anything on this."

"On the contrary," said Mr. LeTourneau, "that's the *first* pledge I shall pay."

He claims that by putting God first, he acquires a source of energy that wouldn't otherwise be available to him.

When you believe that what you are doing is right in the sight of God, you can go ahead with it without having your energies dissipated by an internal battle.

If you think that what you are doing is cheap and stupid and petty, you become exhausted easily.   You then have to fight a continual civil war to convince your conscience that it is all right to do something that you secretly feel is all wrong.

4. Seek scientific guidance

Although your unconscious mind can often suggest the correct goal for your energy, your rational mind should make the *final* decision.

One of the most helpful things you can do to determine the correct vocational goal for you is to get in touch with the nearest university and ask for vocational counseling, which includes a series of aptitude and interest tests.   This counseling is usually available on a non-profit basis, and may cost as little as $35.

A college professor once told me: "Why do you suppose great stores and big corporations make inventories of their assets?   They have at least a vague idea of what they have in stock, but it is important for them to have an exact accounting.

"A man who has aptitudes but doesn't know what they are is like a man with an attic so dark he can't see what is in it. But the moment he turns on an electric light, the attic suddenly becomes illuminated, and he sees every stick of furniture in it. That's what aptitude tests can do for an individual. They do not change the furniture in your mental attic; they just make you aware of what it contains, so you'll know better how to use it."

No matter where you live in the United States, I can recommend an excellent guide for those who want professional counseling on their vocational abilities. This is the Directory of Counseling Agencies, published by the American Personnel and Guidance Association, 1534 "O" Street, N.W., Washington 5, D.C. Its standards are very high. "An approved agency," it states, "does not make use of pseudo-scientific methods, the practice of guidance entirely or mainly by correspondence, the routine practice of counseling in one interview, and the giving of vocational or other advice entirely on the basis of tests."

Approved agencies will usually test both interests and aptitudes. When you find that you have both an interest in and an aptitude for a particular line of work, then you will know just *how* you can wisely direct your energies. If you do work in which you're not interested or for which you have no real aptitude, you'll become exhausted quickly.

In addition, if your work uses only a couple of your aptitudes and you don't find a way of using the others through hobbies, you'll get bored. And when you're bored, you often imagine you are tired. When you imagine you are tired, your available energy is very low.

The world has millions of volts of energy available. You can latch on to some of that magnificent energy, if you wish. But if you don't know what your aptitudes are, it's just as though you were on a street where there were millions of volts of energy, but none of them could be used because all the power lines were down.

When you know what you can do, then power flows to you and through you.

5. Divide your goals

Divide your goals into long-range purposes, medium-term purposes, and immediate goals.

Select as your long-range goal something you like doing. When you really like to do something, you have floating power. Isn't it easier to float than to swim against the tide? Why waste your energy trying to make a career of something you actively dislike?

Many parents and teachers give us the wrong idea about our goals in life. Often we're taught that as a matter of self-discipline, we should choose to do something we hate. Now it's true that doing daily some chore we dislike will give us practice in doing unpleasant things, which is good self-discipline. But the real goal of life, shocking as it may seem to some moralists, is to please, not to displease, ourselves. The greatest pleasure for a mature individual is doing something he likes that will also help others. Doing something you dislike may sometimes be necessary for a few hours. But if your life is dedicated to work you dislike, you're headed for trouble.

In *Try Living* (New York: Thomas Y. Crowell Company, 1937) Dr. William Moulton Marston, the famous psychologist, says he thought seriously of suicide when he was a college student. He believed that success could be attained only by doing something you hated. Under those conditions, life seemed so horrible to him that he obtained some hydro-cyanic acid from a chemist, and made plans to kill himself.

But before he carried out his destructive purpose, he decided to take the mid-year exams to see just how badly he would do. He didn't do too well in most of his exams, but in one, ancient philosophy, taught by a truly inspired teacher, he got an A. He'd loved the subject so much that he had remembered almost every word his professor had ever spoken on it.

Do something you enjoy doing. That was how Dr. Marston learned the lesson that made his life worth living. We usually do best what we *like* to do.

Simple? Well, not quite that simple. There are men who

love to paint, but with whom it will never be anything more than a hobby, because they are not born artists.   There are men who appreciate music and who will always enjoy entertaining their friends with their fiddle or mandolin playing, but who will never be great musicians.

However, if there is something you do easily and well, why not find out if you are good enough to earn a living at it? When you really love to do something, no effort is too hard, and yet the job itself will often seem surprisingly easy.   Our energies flow most readily in the direction of our likes, not our dislikes.

Like your work or learn to like it.   If you haven't the courage to change from a job you dislike, then for Pete's sake try to learn to like it.   Maybe you don't like it because you haven't learned enough about it.   We can't like what we don't understand.   And we can't throw a heap of energy into a job we neither like nor understand.   In fact, in such a case, we waste so much energy hating the job and hating ourselves for not having the courage to walk out on it, that we're continually exhausted.

Select specific financial goals, too.   It will help you to direct your energies properly if, in your pursuit of a long-range goal, you can see yourself achieving medium-sized steps toward that goal.

At the age of 25, a salesman decided to plan his financial goal for the next 40 years.   While still an assistant sales manager, he put $2,000 in a savings bank in a single year, started a $25,000 insurance estate with $600, and invested some of his year-end bonus money in three stocks: a motor, an oil, and a rubber stock.

Before investing his money, he talked with a broker who gave his opinion on whether the price-earnings ratio of each of his intended purchases was a logical one.   He considered this preliminary discussion with a good broker an essential use of time and energy.

Each year, this executive reviews his vocational status and progress, his program for financial security, and his standard of living. Watching his savings grow has given him an added incentive for investing a good proportion of his energy in his work. When you see tangible results from the wise use of energy, you are encouraged to continue pursuing your objectives vigorously.

Just as some employers use prizes as incentive for employees, you can reward yourself with something you greatly desire every time you achieve a goal you have set for yourself. The reward can be a brief trip, a common stock you have wanted to buy, or a new suit—something you will definitely enjoy. The knowledge that such a reward awaits you when you achieve the next step toward your goal will give you additional energy.

How to select a medium-range goal. Your medium-range goal may be a specific plan for the way in which you intend to use your energies in the next six months or the next year. For instance, a California veteran, discovering that a high school diploma is awarded to any veteran who passes the General Educational Test and then takes a certain number of units of history and civics, might decide that winning that diploma is his medium-range goal for the year. Or a salesman might decide that making $100,000 worth of sales is his medium-range goal. Medium-range goals should usually lead by medium-sized steps to your ultimate goals.

Your immediate goal can be planned for a day or a week. In the case of a writer, it might be the writing of a certain number of words, or the completion of a single chapter of a book. In the case of a salesman, it's his daily or weekly quota of sales. A public speaker might wish to make a certain number of speeches a week.

The best method for achieving a short-range goal. It's wise to check on the hours when you do your best work. If your creative energy is greatest during the hours of 8 A.M. to 12:30 P.M., then try to arrange your most creative tasks for those hours. Try to relegate routine jobs to the hours when your energy is at half-mast.

Also, try to do difficult jobs as early in the morning as possible. When you postpone doing them, you rob yourself of energy. The contemplation of a difficult job can rob you of more energy than actually doing it.

So do your most creative job when you are at your peak energy; do your most difficult non-creative job either at the beginning of the day, or right after you have finished the creative chore.

Mental tasks, some authorities say, use very little energy. Maybe so. But they also demand your *freshest* energy. When you are physically or emotionally tired, the portion of your brain that does your finest thinking is weary. Sometimes, it is the first part of your body to tire. So give it your freshest, peak energy. Remember, as we stated in an earlier chapter, you can determine scientifically just when you have this energy by using an ordinary thermometer. At the hour of the day when it is at its highest point, you are at your peak energy point, too. Let the creator in you create at the hour when you are at your most vigorous.

Using your peak energy for difficult tasks will help you achieve your immediate, day-by-day goals. Planning medium-range and long-range goals as targets and reminding yourself of them from week to week will summon energy from deep within you to help you. Your inner mind will release an abundance of energy to you if you give it a purpose in life that makes your unconscious eager to work for you. If you have no such purpose, the unconscious will seek out its own primitive, destructive purpose. Energy *has* to be used.

If it is not directed outward for some useful purpose, it will fester inside you, causing you to become unduly introspective, worried, and fearful.

6. Review your goals at frequent intervals

Sometimes our goals change, as we discover that we don't really want what we thought we wanted. When you feel like changing, don't make the change in too great a hurry. If your goal was thoughtfully chosen in the first place, you may simply have reached a plateau from which it is difficult to progress, and you may be just temporarily discouraged.

The late Dr. William Moulton Marston and I were once discussing a man who abandoned his efforts to get into the field of his choice after four years of trying. I said that I could understand his discouragement, and that in his place, I, too, would have quit after four years.

"Would you?" said Dr. Marston. "I wouldn't. If you're starving, of course it's all right to take a temporary job in a different field than that into which you'd hoped to get. But you shouldn't abandon your efforts completely. The results of four years of effort may just be about to show up at such a time. No one should abandon permanently the fruits of his efforts till the decision is forced on him."

In reviewing your goals, if you chose them sensibly in the first place, your main concern should be with whether or not your desires have changed. Occasionally, as we mature, we do set our hearts on more mature goals. But we should never abandon a goal just because it is difficult to achieve.

Reviewing our goals is important because our energies should be logically directed toward what we really want, not something that we once wanted and no longer care about.

7. Visualize yourself achieving your goal

It always takes less energy to accomplish what you can visualize yourself achieving than what you consider difficult or impossible.

A very wise man named Baudoin once wrote: "To be ambitious for wealth, and yet always expecting to be poor; to be always doubting your ability to get what you long for, is like trying to reach east by traveling west. There is no philosophy which will help a man to succeed when he is always doubting his ability to do so, and thus attracting failure."

Doubts subtract from your energy. They exhaust you. Sometimes they may even keep you from taking the necessary first step that will enable you to reach your goal.

"Our doubts are traitors," Shakespeare once wrote.

He was right.

Don't nourish that traitor!

Your *real* expectations can materialize. Visualize yourself in possession of the success you desire. But do not substitute the magic of *believing* for the magic of *doing*. You may need a little of the magic of believing to release your energy. But that energy is of no use to you until you use it.

8. Take at least one step toward your goal today

In her charming book, *Forever Young, Forever Healthy* (Englewood Cliffs, N. J.: Prentice-Hall, Inc., 1953), Indra Devi tells the story of a woman who made up her mind that she wanted a Cadillac. So she visualized one in her garage. However, the only step she took toward making the dream a reality was to speculate on the stock market. Her speculation was badly chosen. For she had not devoted any of her energy to learning the difference between a reckless speculation and an investment. She had just plunged blindly.

In the course of time, she lost the money with which she had speculated. By this time she had dissipated most of her savings and she had to sell the luxurious home in which she had lived, and rent a little apartment across the street from it. Each day from her apartment window she could see the people who had bought her home. In their garage was the Cadillac she had lovingly visualized. It was just where she had visualized it. But it was theirs, not hers.

I once discussed Indra Devi's story with a student of the art of thought. She said: "The woman Miss Devi told about did not visualize enough of the details. She should have pictured her right hand on the Cadillac, caressing it, and in her left hand a pink slip, showing that *she* owned the Cadillac."

"Uh, huh," I said. "That might have helped. But in addition, I think she should have done something to earn the money for the car."

HOW TO CHANGE UNDESIRABLE GOALS TO DESIRABLE ONES

The power of thought can give us a tremendous shove in the right direction. We visualize or emotionalize. Then the unconscious mind gets busy on the product we are visualizing. It decides whether the goal we claim to clamor for is one *it* really desires. When we are children the unconscious mind first sets its goals. They may be stupid; they may be destructive; they may be dangerous. But they can be *changed!*

Sometimes, if we've gone far enough in the wrong direction, only a psychiatrist can help us find the right one for our energies.

At other times, when we look at what our goals (partly unconscious) have done to us, we can yank ourselves in an opposite direction.

A businessman who had drunk himself into failure was prevailed upon by his wife to go with her to a sermon by Dr. Ernest Holmes. In it he talked of the various ways in which men and women destroy everything worth-while in their lives.

"God," he said, "puts normal, healthy, intelligent individuals on earth with talents and abilities He wants them to use. However, if we don't open our minds to the great Source of all good, we may end up spending our lives tearing down the great abilities He has given us." He pointed out that it was possible to spend the energy God has given us in destroying everything worth-while in our lives.

For this special occasion, the businessman had remained sober. "Why, Ernest Holmes is talking directly to me," he thought. "God hasn't been making a failure out of me. I've been making one out of myself."

That week, he joined the local AA group, and learned that an alcoholic is never cured of his alcoholism, but can learn to do without alcohol. Today that former alcoholic is the head of one of the biggest businesses in the United States. Very few of his associates know anything of his background.

By using his energy constructively instead of destructively he was able to fulfill every good dream he had ever had.

You, too, can fulfill yours.

The chances are that you are not an alcoholic. But if you are a victim of chronic fatigue, you may be throwing your energy down some other destructive path.

You have all the energy you need to accomplish anything within reason.

In fact, you may have too much energy.   It is the overflow of energy into the wrong channels that messes up so many lives.   You and only you can channel it so it serves you instead of using you.

The energy is there, waiting to be used.

It's there, even if it's flowing into personal hate, bitterness, revenge, hostility.

It's possible to take all those emotions and change them into aggressive, fighting energy, useful in competitive business. Usually, however, even if you use these emotions to get ahead of your competitors for a while, they will in the end destroy you.   Hate creates hate.

So if you want to avoid mental illness, such as great personal hatred eventually brings, don't depend on hatred and revenge as motive powers for you.   Directed against any individual, they are too dangerous.

If you dislike someone, bless him in your thoughts, if possible; pray for him; forgive him.   Try to do something for him if you possibly can.

Don't think I'm advising you to be noble or a saint.   My suggestion is that you do these things mainly for selfish reasons: so that you may survive and stay mentally healthy.   It's difficult to try to help those we dislike.   But hating others can make us sick; it can leave us with very little energy.   So for our own sakes, we have to try to cure ourselves of some of our personal hatreds.   We can't do it by suppressing that hate, or pretending we like people we can barely stand.

However, Professor Pitirim A. Sorokin of the Harvard Research Center in Creative Altruism discovered that when we try to help others, we lose our intense dislike of them, and sometimes end up by liking them.

Liking many individuals and wanting to help them as well as yourself is a great source of energy.

Be selfish, but be intelligently selfish.   Anyone who doesn't consider the ultimate effect of his actions on himself is either a saint (of whom there are very few) or a darned fool.

If you are intelligently selfish, you will devote a certain amount of your energy to achieving your own goals, and a certain amount to helping others.

If you want energy, you cannot accept the feeling that you are of no importance in God's universe. You must realize that you are important, that you have talents and abilities, and can use them in a manner that might help others.

Don't hoard your energy. Only by using your energy can you have more energy! We are not wild animals who can gain energy by hibernating. We must step out and live every day, every hour, every minute.

In the next chapter, we'll tell you how you can harness your energy so as to start living immediately. And we'll talk about exactly how, when, and where to use your second wind.

POINTS YOU'LL WANT TO REMEMBER

1. Analyze yourself to find out what your greatest drives are.

2. Build up your craving for any goal you choose, by thinking about that goal and writing it down.

3. Pray for guidance in using your energy to do God's will, instead of expecting Him to do yours.

4. Seek scientific guidance on your abilities, aptitudes, and interests.

5. Select a long-range goal to which you'll enjoy directing your energies. Then figure out medium-term and short-term goals that will help you achieve your distant goal.

6. Review your goals at frequent intervals.

7. Visualize yourself achieving your goal.

8. Today take at least one step toward a goal you have consciously chosen.

9. Don't hoard your energy.

10. Try to do something helpful for someone you don't like very much.

12

A 10-Point Blueprint for Whipping That Tired Feeling

IF YOU ARE GOING TO LIVE ENERGETICALLY, YOU MUST START today. It's a common practice to procrastinate. Most of us are filled with good resolves that could change our lives for the better. But if we don't act on them immediately, we may never act on them at all.

God's gift of the present moment must be used wisely. Goethe, the great poet, once said: "Be always resolute with the present. Every moment is of infinite value, for it is the representative of eternity."

Do you want to be whipped by that tired feeling? Then put off till tomorrow or the next day a change in your program of living.

To brim over with energy, you must draw up a new blueprint for your life today—if possible, the minute you finish reading this chapter.

Here is a 10-point blueprint by which you can whip that tired feeling instead of having it whip you.

1. A practical aid

Use "Who," "What," "When," and "Where" cards to show you how to channel your energy.

190

Use a series of four by six cards, or if you don't have them handy, four sheets of paper from an ordinary pad. On one sheet or card write "Who," on a second "What," on a third "When," and on a fourth "Where."

On the card labelled "Who," list from five to ten of the most important individuals in your life at present. Write down this question: Who adds to my energy? Write down the names of those close to you who in some way, perhaps by their encouragement or by their positive attitude toward life, add to your energy whenever you spend time with them.

Your next list, which you can put on the other side of the four by six card, is your frank answer to the question: Who subtracts from my energy?

From now on, you resolve, you will spend more and more time with those who add to your energy by their positive attitudes. You will spend less time with those whose attitudes are destructive, carping, and negative.

You cannot always cut negative individuals completely out of your life. Some friend of yours may be going through a very trying period, and need your support, even though you can give it only at a great cost in energy. Or you may have some relative who is so close you feel a bond of duty, even though you must listen every day to his whining series of complaints. If this relative is actually affecting your mental health, you may have to see a compassionate outsider, a minister or doctor, who will let you know exactly how much of your energy you are duty bound to let go down the drain.

How to diminish the effect of negative personalities. I know of one man whose mother had become such a whining, malicious person that she was a threat to his marriage, as well as to his energy. Every single day she insisted on finding excuses to consult him, sometimes about trivial matters—anything so she could tear him away from his wife and children. Her own husband was dead, and she had never had the foresight or wisdom to build up any interest in her later years except possessing her son's mind, heart, and soul.

She was constantly making bitter, cruel, and false accusations against his wife. Finally, the wife took a firm stand.

"You're going to have to choose between your mother and me," she said. "You have never truly left your mother, and she has never allowed you to have a life of your own.

"If you want to see her once a week, fine. But if you must spend hours every day with her, giving you virtually no time to be with the children or myself, then we'll have to separate."

The man consulted his minister, who agreed with the wife that marriage comes first. He quoted from the Bible: "For this cause shall a man leave his father and mother, and shall be joined unto his wife, and they two shall be one flesh."

The husband told his mother that he would be able to see her only once a week. At first she took her son's dwindling interest in her companionship hard, and made many scenes. But she finally accepted his decision, and learned to adjust herself to the people around her, instead of depending completely on him for an interest in life.

Spend less and less time with negative individuals. After he had freed himself from his mother's over-demanding personality, this man found that his energy was able to flow into new and delightful paths. He could go fishing with his sons once a week. He became a leader in the Boy Scout group to which one of his boys belonged, and the family began going on frequent picnics, finding true joy in togetherness. Because he was no longer in a state of mental conflict over how much time he owed his mother, he was full of energy all day, and ready to go to sleep the moment his head hit the pillow.

So if someone, even a close relative, is having a drastic negative effect on your energy, make up your mind to spend less time with him. Compel him either to take a less destructive attitude, or cut him or her out of your life as much as possible.

So much for "Who"—who is lightening your load by a cheerful attitude, and who is tearing down your energy. Face the facts, and do something about them. We all want to be helpful to our friends. But this doesn't include being two bit psychiatrists and trying to change attitudes that need the services of a professional counselor.

After finishing your "Who" card, prepare "When," "Where,"

and "What" cards. On your "When" card schedule today's activities for every half hour of the day till the time you go to bed in the evening. If you haven't seen your doctor for the past year, be sure to include on today's schedule a telephone call requesting an appointment for a physical examination. This will help you determine whether there is any physical factor that should be cleared up to restore your buoyant energy.

Your "Where" card should be a plan for making whatever calls you have to by a convenient route, with the least possible waste of energy.

On your "What" card make two lists: *What Adds to Energy,* and *What Subtracts.* If you are not sure of some item on one of these lists, put a question mark next to it, and make up your mind to check your reactions carefully for the next month to find out if this particular item does subtract from your energy.

Today you are going to try to avoid every factor that seems to subtract from your energy, unless it adds tremendously to your achievements.

2. Use your imagination

Use your imagination to assist your will power in destroying anything that threatens to use your energy negatively.

Harness your imagination. When our parents taught us, "Where there's a will there's a way" they neglected to tell us what the way was. Actually it's simple. The will cannot function properly without a powerful, constructive imagination. Your imagination, properly used, can show you how to channel your energy. Your will power is weak without its help.

Arthur, a lawyer, had an indulgent wife. Perhaps, in some respects, she was too indulgent. She allowed him to keep very irregular hours.

When he was 45, he decided that he hadn't had enough sex adventure in his life. His middle-aged eyes began roaming the field. Whenever he found a young woman who might be attracted to him, he made a play for her.

His adventures as a middle-aged Don Juan fed his ego.

But the feeding was just temporary. Each time an adventure was finished, he sought another. He needed constant reassurance that he wasn't aging, that he was attractive enough to win the hearts of young and lovely women.

In his imagination, he always saw himself as an eager, attractive Lothario. He did not picture the possible unhappy consequences of his sexual indulgences.

When he finally engaged in an affair with one of his wife's best friends, she told him she'd had enough. She sued for divorce, taking their three children with her.

His imagination had never pictured such a consequence.

He went on his knees, begging for forgiveness, and it was finally granted.

But something vital had gone out of their marriage. Now he had real cause for feeling frustrated. Instead of seeking the help of a marriage counselor, he went back to the habit of many amours.

Why was his resolve so weak? Why didn't he stick by his marriage vows?

To say that his will power was weak is begging the question. It would be more truthful to say that he had never uncovered the real reason for his Don Juan complex. In each love adventure, he was trying to convince himself of his own masculinity. Perhaps he needed a psychiatrist to help him find out why he had to prove this point to himself.

In addition, he harnessed his imagination to *untruths.* Each time he told himself: "It doesn't really matter. My wife won't find out. I'm not really harming anybody." Eventually his wife left him for good.

How to use your imagination to create more energy. He had used his imagination to help destroy his life. He had used a warped imagination in such a way as to lose his children's respect. It also cost him many clients, for news of such derelictions often travels by grapevine into many places.

A powerful imagination, rightly used, can show a man of weak resolve the destruction he is sowing all around him through his actions. It also can show him how pleasant life

can be for his loved ones and himself if he will only replace his
bad habit with a better one.   Used this way, imagination becomes a great source for energy.

It makes little difference whether the bad habit relates to
sex, alcohol, compulsive eating, addiction to sleeping pills, or
compulsive gambling.   To get rid of it, don't just grit your
teeth, clench your jaws, and make a noble resolve.   The resolves will melt like snows in the summertime unless you let
your imagination project you into the wonderful world of it-
can-be.

If you have a habit that is tearing down your energy, promise yourself that tonight when you go to bed, as you are drifting off to sleep, you will picture in your mind the triumphant
conquest of that habit.

Never permit an exception to occur.   Every time we indulge
in a bad habit, as William James pointed out, our molecules
and nerve centers count the slip.   We say to ourselves, "Well,
next time I won't slip again," but each slip makes the next
attempt to break the habit more difficult.

You can break it.   Disuse is the best way to break any habit.
Complete disuse.   If your doctor agrees that the habit is one
that can and should be broken, take his advice.   Add to it a
little imaginative spice.   Picture yourself as the triumphant
individual you will be when you have conquered your own
destructive habits completely.   Find something constructive to
replace it, like the mastery of a new sport or hobby.

3. Try a seven day positive thinking program

Start your own personal Mental Health week.   Try, for at
least a week, starting right now, the effect of positive thought
and buoyant action.   Do not during this week permit any
negative thought to remain in your mind.   Remember the old
Chinese proverb: Bats may fly over your head, but you do not
have to let them nest in your hair.

If someone says to you: "You can't," "That's impossible,"
"You can't win for losing," "You're too old," or "You'll never
make it," don't accept his negative thoughts passively.   Con-

sider each negative a challenge to you, to prove the opposite, positive thought.   Substitute a positive emotion for every negative thought thrown at you by anyone, including yourself.

For every negative thought you hear, do some research to try to discover a positive fact.

For instance, if someone tells you that individuals lose most of their mental powers after the age of 50, look up the facts. IQ tests show that older individuals think just as clearly or more clearly than younger folk, though they may be at a slight disadvantage where speed is concerned.   And what of such wise old men as Herbert Hoover, writing best sellers at 84, or the late Dr. Albert Einstein, working out complicated scientific theories after 65?

Once you have practiced positive thinking for an entire week, you'll want to practice it for *all* the weeks of your life.

Here are some ways of doing so.   Before you go to bed at night, search your mind to remember your happiest experience of the day.   When you wake up, wake up expecting the day to be a happy one.   Get frequent hunches that something wonderful is going to happen within the next week or the next month.   It is amazing how much such happy expectations influence the events of your life.

When you are filled with gloomy forebodings about the future, you cannot whip up much energy.   Transform fear of the future into action in the present, and you'll have a great deal of energy.   In fact, one of the few values fear has is to enable you to whip up the energy for action.

4. Change your negative feelings

Change your negative feelings by changing the expressions of your face, the postures of your body, and your verbal expressions.

We cannot always control feelings directly.   We can usually control them indirectly by learning to practice a sunny smile, a buoyant walk, and the use of optimistic words instead of destructive verbiage in describing our problems.

If you want energy to spare, don't use negative words.   "I

can't take it . . . I just don't know how I can go on . . . I've
lost everything" are the expressions used by those who want
excuses for not facing up to life's challenges.

"I can do it . . . It sounds like a very challenging job . . .
Just try me" are some of the expressions used by those who
want to build up their energy. If you regard every obstacle
as a challenge, your glands will pour forth the hormones you
need to meet those challenges.

Now what about the physical expression of your feelings?
The late Dr. James Wood, an internationally famous educa-
tor, who was president of Stephens College for many years, had
a wonderful philosophy about this.

He once said, "My father had a laugh that rang over the
whole countryside. He had lots of problems, but just the same,
his laugh used to bellow from him loudly and boisterously as
though he didn't have a worry in the world. One night I
asked him why he laughed so loudly in the face of so many
problems."

Advice on how to face one's deepest problems. " 'My boy,'
he said, 'remember this always, the world is not keenly interested in your problems. When they are the deepest, let your
laughter be the loudest!' "

This advice is certainly difficult to carry out, but those who
live up to it become much greater individuals. One day I
met a man who had lived up to this philosophy. A former
political prisoner in Asia, he had come out of a concentration
camp looking like a scarecrow. His wife and two children
had been imprisoned in a separate camp. Reunited, they set
out to face the world with gratitude for their deliverance.

He started a new career in public relations in Canada. He
and his wife had a baby son. When the child was only a year
old, he died of spinal meningitis.

The family could have been felled by self-pity. In Canada,
they couldn't forget what had happened to their child, so they
moved to the United States, where the father got another excellent public relations job.

One day he told me, "Most people who meet me think I'm a

very happy-go-lucky man. They say, 'Sammy doesn't have a care in the world.' My wife and I go to parties, where we have as good a time as possible. I'm always laughing. At work, I give all my energy to the job.

"Underneath our happy laughter, we are haunted by a memory we'll never forget. But we will continue to express happiness whenever we can—for the sake of our two children, and so that we may have energy to make the most of the rest of our lives."

Had Samuel yielded to self-pity, he would not have had enough energy to adapt himself to a new life in a new world. But instead he faced his acquaintances with as much outward cheer as possible.

If he, with his sad memories, could do it, what about you and me? Is there anything to keep us from facing the world as sunnily as possibly, and thereby promoting our own energy as well as cheering up our neighbors?

5. Act as if you were self-confident

Always do what you think a self-confident person would do.

If lack of self-confidence is corroding your energy, reread Chapter 4.

Describe on a sheet of paper the manner in which you feel a self-confident person would tackle your problems. Read that sheet of paper when you have completed your description. When you go to bed at night, say to yourself, "From now on, I shall behave more and more like the self-confident person I am going to be."

6. When expressing anger . . .

Before you allow yourself to get angry, be sure that the source of your anger is worth the emotion.

Trying to suppress emotions is dangerous. But just as in jurisprudence, the punishment should fit the crime, so every emotion you allow yourself to indulge in should be appropriate. There's no use wasting one hundred dollars' worth of energy on a two-bit irritation. If you find yourself flying off the handle because of little things, you may be suffering from a basic frustration or sense of insecurity. Try to find out the real cause of your irritability, for anger and irritability are exhausting emotions.

As a young boy, Bernard Baruch used to fly into a tantrum at the slightest provocation. Basically, this was because he was unsure of himself, and not able to handle himself well in a fight with other boys. He fought frequently, and was licked frequently, too.

Then when he became of college age, he went in for athletics, learned to defend himself. As he became more sure of his physical prowess, he was less frustrated, and therefore got angry much less often.

Too frequent tantrums are not only a drain on energy, but also a confession of inadequacy. Try to find out what inadequacy sensed in yourself causes you to blow up easily. Then try to remedy the real frustration.

7. Conquer the habit of worrying excessively

If you have any current worry, write it down on a card or slip of paper. Write down what, if anything, you can do about it. Then start doing it.

If you have a worry that permits of no adequate solution, try to compensate for it by doing something constructive. For instance, if some dearly loved relative were to become mentally ill, you would naturally try to get psychiatric help for him. When you were sure that everything possible was being done for him, you could make additional constructive use of your energy by joining your local Mental Health Association and offering to do volunteer work for it, such as raising money for its campaigns.

8. Try to get rid of unnecessary guilt feelings

If you are troubled by something you have done, try to make amends for it as quickly as possible. If you can make amends today, do so. Otherwise resolve to make them at the first possible opportunity.

If you have profound guilt feelings, and do not know why you have them, ask your doctor for the name of a good clinical psychologist or psychiatrist. Then phone for a consultation.

9. List your goals in life

Make a list of your important goals in life, and take at least one step today toward fulfilling one or more of those goals.

Big goals toward which you strive realistically have the power, some wise person once said, to stir the blood (and of course your energy). Petty goals rarely have such blood-stirring, energy-stirring powers. But many of us are so constituted that it is difficult for us to believe that we can reach the big goals unless we reach many small stations on the way. So figure out some small goals on the way, too.

Make peace of mind one of your big goals. In making up your own personal list, remember that the greatest sages have always pointed out the importance of putting either peace of mind or mental health (which includes religious faith) at the top of your list.

The Bible says: "What shall it profit a man if he gain the whole world and lose his own soul?"

Better be whole than holy. Though psychiatrists may substitute another word for "soul," they are in agreement with ministers on this subject. A psychiatrist might say: "What shall it profit a man if he gain the whole world and lose his sense of being an integrated personality?" Ministers wise in the ways of psychiatry know that while a few may strive to be "holy," most of us must be "whole" in order to use our energies for worth-while purposes.

A healthy religion should be part of your life. A kind and spiritual attitude toward your fellow men, but one without fanaticism, can very well be one of your ten greatest goals in life. Your most important life purposes should include physical health; love and possibly marriage; happy friendships; the achievement of a sensible amount of work; a certain amount of education or do-it-yourself learning; and a sensible amount of social life.

Tie up today's schedule with your permanent goals. When you have finished your list of what you consider your ten most important permanent goals, take another look at your schedule for today. Just how does each item in your schedule tie up with your permanent goals? Next to each item on it you should place the number of the goal it will help you to reach. For instance, if making and keeping friends is the fourth item on your list, put the number 4 next to those hours you are going to spend with friends.

Check your schedule for today and for this coming week to see if you have allowed enough time for your important goals. If you don't give time and energy to them, how can you expect to attain them? If you say that marital happiness is one of your ten great goals, how much time have you allowed yourself to spend with your wife and children today? How much for the rest of this week? Don't kid yourself by saying that you work 15 hours every day to make your wife happy. Something is wrong with either you or your wife if it takes 15 or more hours a day to earn enough money to keep her contented. Is it possible that you are putting material possessions at the very top of your mental list, instead of giving them a more subordinate position?

Every single item in your schedule for a day or a week should be related to a permanent purpose. If you are spending six hours today on an item that doesn't appear on your list, ask yourself why your actual schedule is so contrary to your statement of purposes. Is this just a peculiarity for today, or have you drifted into the habit of spending time on worthless activities?

Include pleasure or social life among your goals. This doesn't mean that you should not have some fun in your life. Social life can very well be among your ten greatest aims. It's doubtful that it should ever be number one on your list. The playboy who spends 16 hours a day in the pursuit of pleasure rarely finds it.

When your goals are followed with all your heart and with all your desires, they will lend wings to your energy.

10. Learn to use a "second wind" for emergencies

Most of us, William James once pointed out, make it a habit to stop an occupation as soon as we have reached the first layer of fatigue. But if a crisis compels us to go ahead, even though we imagine we have walked, played, or worked "enough," the fatigue suddenly passes away, and we draw on mysterious reserve energy. This is a level of new energy that we ordinarily don't reach. "There may be layer after layer of this experience," William James has said. "A third and a fourth 'wind' may supervene."

You, the possessor of this second, third, and fourth wind, are in the position of a man who has a certain amount of cash on hand but who also has hidden check accounts on which he can draw whenever he really needs them.

FOUR SUGGESTIONS ON TAPPING THIS SECOND WIND

1. Autocondition your mind or use autosuggestion

In *Autoconditioning, the New Way to A Successful Life,* Hornell Hart, Ph.D., tells the story of a graduate student in sociology who agreed to write a term thesis on Pareto. All term his research engrossed him, but he didn't do any actual writing on the thesis until 12 hours before the paper was due.

Ordinarily, writing such a thesis might require the expenditure of days, perhaps weeks of work. But John Merck, the student, decided he would write it in less than 12 hours. In his psychology class he had learned the art of autoconditioning.

He followed instructions for autoconditioning, then told his unconscious mind: "You will feel wide-awake, energetic, and enthusiastic from now until 4 A.M. At four you will feel sleepy and go to bed. You will wake promptly at seven thirty, and feel fresh, vigorous, and energetic until you have delivered the paper to your professor."

He followed these directions almost exactly, except that he

went to bed at 4:30 A.M. instead of at 4 A.M. He completed the thesis in time, and his professor remarked on what a fine piece of work it was.

Don't whip your mind into super-action every day. In an emergency, undreamed of powers and energy can come to our aid. But emergency powers should usually be saved for emergencies.

2. Keep talk of your plans to a minimum

Don't talk about your plans any more than you absolutely have to.

Your energy can be dissolved, like so much steam, into the empty air, if you talk too much about your plans. If you are going to write, write. If you are going to sell, sell. If you are going to invent, invent. That doesn't mean, of course, that you shouldn't *plan* all these activities. The more carefully you blueprint exactly what you plan to do or outline what you are going to write, the more likely you are to be able to proceed with the actual work without hindrance or doubts. But spend no more time *talking* about your plans than you absolutely *must* in order to sell the idea to your supervisor or boss.

The unconscious mind can be lazy or energetic, according to how you handle it. Crack that whip! Make it behave. If you tell all the details of the novel you plan to write to your friends, your unconscious will have gotten out of you all it ever wants to get—self-expression. If you have a wonderful idea for an invention, don't describe the details to anyone. If you do, your unconscious mind may find itself released from the onerous job of creating the invention.

Don't talk away your energy. You can use the energy of the unconscious to create. If you have any big problem, say today to the genie of the unconscious mind, after you have surveyed your problem: "A solution please by a week from Saturday." More often than not, the unconscious mind will find its way through a labyrinth of facts to present you with a worth-while answer.

By using your unconscious mind to get the answers, you not only frequently get better answers, but get them with much less effort. Socrates used to say that without his "daemon" (meaning his inner mind) all his great achievements would have been impossible.

By using the energy of the unconscious, you save your energy. But if you waste your effectiveness in a lot of high-sounding talk, the unconscious will drift into lethargy. Unless your job is lecturing, don't talk away the greater part of your energy. Haven't you ever found that after describing your magnificent plans to your friends, you feel such pleasure in having talked about them, that there is no longer need to act?

You'll never have a second wind, unless you learn how to dam up your energy by not talking too much about what you are going to do. This gives you a second wind for action, not talk.

3. Learn to use the three inciters of energy

What else can we do to stimulate our energy to go beyond the first fatigue limits inertia sets up for us? William James recommends three inciters of energy: excitement, ideas, and effort.

Emotional excitement nearly always produces additional energy. In *How Power Selling Brought Me Success in 6 Hours* (Englewood Cliffs, N. J.: Prentice-Hall, Inc., 1954) Dr. Pierce P. Brooks tells us that for 20 years he had coasted along doing what he thought was the best he could. Then suddenly he lost his job. His contract as an insurance agent, which was his only source of income, was suddenly cancelled.

His back was to the wall. Either he had to tell his salesmen that he had no more work for them and lose all of them, or he had to find a solution within 24 hours.

His solution was to act as if he had nothing to lose, thus giving him a source of power he had never had previously. Most of us lose 25 per cent of our energy worrying about what might happen if we acted resolutely.

Thus by deciding to act as if he had nothing to lose, Dr. Brooks had at least a 25 per cent energy gain. He used his energy to work out a great sales pitch; then he used more energy to put that pitch across over the telephone. Pouring all his power and enthusiasm into his sales pitch, he made a series of telephone calls to men with the money to invest in a new company. By 4 A.M., he had $37,000 pledged to start an insurance company that later rocketed into one of the biggest in the country.

How to build up the right amount of excitement. Where did the magic energy come from? From the excitement of feeling he faced a crisis. Later a friend of his, Frank Pace, Former Secretary of the Army, told him how *each* of us can summon up extra energy every day. Mr. Pace said: "Most of us are unable to see that every day is critical. We kid ourselves that we are not involved in a crisis, just because everything is quiet and we seem to be getting by all right at the moment. But the truth is that we are continually on the spot if we could but see it. What we do or don't do in the present moment is going to be terribly important to our future happiness and fortune . . . Each minute is an opportunity."

Get excited about something today. Fasten your attention on it. Realize how important it can be to your future. Don't be jittery about it, but make up your mind you will do the best you can.

Ideas produce new energy. If you can become excited about an idea, you will have two important stimulators of energy: ideas and excitements. Learn to demand ideas from your unconscious mind. Whatever your problems for tomorrow are going to be, ask your unconscious mind, before you drop off to sleep tonight, to help you solve them. Command it gently but firmly.

When you wake up the following morning with an idea, don't examine it critically at first. Allow yourself to become enthusiastic about it. This will give you additional energy with which to carry out your idea, until you have perfected some of the details. Do not submit it to anyone for critical examination until a week or more has passed.

Effort sometimes produces energy. We often quit too soon because we're not willing to put out enough effort. The salesman who succeeds seems to have more energy than the one who fails, for instance. Why? Is it possible that his greater efforts produced energy, and that energy then in turn produced more effort?

I have heard some very successful salesmen say that their best orders often came the fourth time they tried. The determination to try four times instead of just once, or to make 12 calls a day instead of 10 will give you extra energy.

4. Plan ahead of time

Sometimes the energy you spend on preparation will save you from wasting an enormous amount of energy on fruitless work and useless effort. This results in more successful use of your efforts. When you find you are more successful, that in turn gives you more energy. As you know, failure can make you quite despondent, and lessen your energy. So to have superior energy, you must stack the cards so that you will have more successes than failures. That means that no matter what your field is, you'll be wise to devote a greater proportion of time and effort to planning.

Most jobs can be done with far less effort if they are well-planned in advance. Sticking strictly to trial and error methods is for the birds—and usually the less intelligent birds at that.

To most of the creatures of the forest, Nature gives divine instincts so that they won't have to rely on haphazard methods to determine how and where to feed, and how to survive.

To man, God gave not only instincts but a mind capable of high development. So why shouldn't we use the sense God gave us to plan each important job, before we start on it?

Give more of your effort to planning, and you'll be able to work your plans. For instance, the most successful salesman I know devotes more of his time to planning how he will handle his sales calls than he does to the actual calls themselves. When he meets one of his sales prospects, he has so much advance knowledge of the man's business that he can point out exactly how his product can be tailored to help this particular individual and his firm.

If, like this man, you start living calmly, confidently, and with the knowledge that you will achieve your goals, you'll stop feeling tired. Of course, you may feel temporarily wilted when nature gives you the signal to rest at night. But this will be the normal, happy tiredness that paves the way for more energy tomorrow.

When you go to bed tonight, say to yourself: "Tomorrow I shall have all the energy I need to accomplish anything necessary to help me reach my goals. I shall be amazed at the ease with which I get things accomplished."

And so help me, you will be amazed!

YOUR 10 POINT BLUEPRINT SUMMARIZED

1. Use "Who," "What," "When," and "Where" cards to show you how to channel your energy.

2. Use your imagination to assist your will power in replacing any habit that requires a destructive use of energy.

3. Try a seven-day positive thinking program.

4. Change your negative feelings by changing the expressions of your face, the postures of your body, and your verbal expressions to positive, happy ones.

5. Always act in any situation as you think a self-confident person would.

6. Try to avoid getting angry about trifles. If you have a tendency to be irritated by little things, try to find out what frustration makes you so susceptible to irritability, and then try to eliminate the cause of that frustration.

7. Try to conquer the habit of worrying excessively.

8. Try to get rid of excessive guilt feelings. If you are troubled by something you have actually done, make amends if possible as quickly as you can. If you cannot trace the guilt feeling to any definite cause, talk to your doctor, asking him to recommend a psychologist or psychiatrist.

9. Make a list of your important goals in life, and take at least one step today toward fulfilling one of those goals.

10. When you are faced with an emergency, learn to use

*your "second wind" of energy.   You can whip that tired feel-
ing through the use of excitement, energy, and effort.   You
are the possessor not only of a "cash" account of energy that
you use every day, but of great reserves of energy you rarely
draw on.   Keep those reserves ready always for emergency
use.*

STOP FEELING TIRED AND START LIVING, TODAY!

Index

M

STOP FEELING TIRED
and
START LIVING

by DORA ALBERT

What keeps most people from accomplishing the things they want to do? What makes them "pooped out" nine days out of ten—half-defeated by the time they get out of bed?

In most cases, the author shows, it is because they actually destroy their own energy!

In this fascinating and important book you are going to see:

WHY you can make yourself feel tired

WHAT to do about breaking the habit

HOW to live all your life on a high plane of energy, achievement and peace of mind

In Part One, Dora Albert asks *Why get tired?* When you have explored this question—and found out some rather startling, scientific discoveries about fatigue and human nature—you see how to build up your energy by changing a habit of thinking. (If you think this is strange, remember some occasion when your tiredness vanished because you were happily excited . . . *in your mind)*

In Part Two, you see how certain uncontrolled emotions can make you squander your energy just as surely as though you threw it away. You see how to turn your anger-energy, for instance, into constructive channels. How even an over-aggressive person, without becoming a